Business Plan for the Proc

Diana Pineda

Business Plan for the Production and Marketing of a Wine

Creation of an Orange Wine

ScienciaScripts

Imprint

Any brand names and product names mentioned in this book are subject to trademark, brand or patent protection and are trademarks or registered trademarks of their respective holders. The use of brand names, product names, common names, trade names, product descriptions etc. even without a particular marking in this work is in no way to be construed to mean that such names may be regarded as unrestricted in respect of trademark and brand protection legislation and could thus be used by anyone.

Cover image: www.ingimage.com

This book is a translation from the original published under ISBN 978-620-0-01573-0.

Publisher:
Sciencia Scripts
is a trademark of
Dodo Books Indian Ocean Ltd. and OmniScriptum S.R.L publishing group

120 High Road, East Finchley, London, N2 9ED, United Kingdom
Str. Armeneasca 28/1, office 1, Chisinau MD-2012, Republic of Moldova, Europe

ISBN: 978-620-6-98844-1

BUSINESS PLAN FOR PRODUCTION AND COMMERCIALIZATION

WINE

AUTHORS:

MARIA FERNANDA LADINES

LADINES DIANA ELIZABETH PINEDA

SANCHEZ.

LETTERS.

I dedicate this work to **God** for allowing me to reach this point, giving me the strength to achieve my goals, setting me on the path of goodness, and putting in my path those people who have been my support and companion throughout my training.

To my mother **Christina Ladines** for her constant support, her advice, values and constant motivation that made it possible for me to complete my studies.

Maria Fernanda Ladinez Ladinez

"Your talent will be lacking if you don't develop it, if you don't study, if you don't work hard, if you don't

you're dedicated to getting better every day.

Will Smith

LETTERS.

I dedicate this work first of all to God, who helped me to advance on this path and gave me the strength to go forward and never go back. To him all glory and honor, because he deserves it, and without him I am nothing.

And also to my parents, who have been the foundation of my life, instilling in me the values and principles that have allowed me to pursue my career. To my beloved husband, who was with me in good times and bad, and together we moved forward in all circumstances, where he always gave me his support and faith, even when I didn't have it.

"I can do all things through Christ who strengthens me."

Philippians 4:13

Diana Elizabeth Pineda Sanchez

THANK YOU

To God for giving me the strength I need each day to keep going, teaching me that every effort is worth it.

To my mom for being the only person who supported me unconditionally throughout this journey. This achievement is not only mine, it belongs to both of us, and with God's blessing we will achieve many more achievements in the future.

To my friends who I have met throughout my college career, with whom I have shared many important moments and know that better times and triumphs are yet to come, it is hard to mention anyone because I can honestly say that the list is very long, although there are some that are more special than others.

To my thesis mentor Ing. Jaime Paez for passing on his knowledge and for telling me, "Mafer, don't let me lose my way."

To my teachers who passed on their knowledge to me during the four years of my university career, to my beloved Department of Chemical Engineering and to my alma mater, the University of Guayaquil.

And finally, I want to thank someone special, that friend, almost sister, who has been a part of my life for many years - endless thanks for everything Viviana Jimenez.

Maria Fernanda Ladinez Ladinez

ABSTRACT

The purpose of this project is to create a company for the production and sale of orange wine, located in the canton of Caluma, province of Bolivar, Sierra region, which aims to offer society a quality and useful product during consumption. The thesis describes in detail the problem to be investigated, considering it as a business opportunity. The history of the research, the origin of wine, the components and classes of wine are also described. A specific presentation of the company and its product, a market analysis, a marketing plan, a technical study and finally an administrative study are presented. The financial study deals with the overall investment in fixed assets, investment in variable, fixed and administrative costs. The start-up status, income statement, cash flow and financial estimates of NPV and IRR are described in detail.

Keywords: Production, quality, entrepreneurship, market, fermentation.

TABLE OF CONTENTS

INTRODUCTION

Wine is a beverage resulting from the alcoholic fermentation of must or fruit juice, which is produced by the metabolic reaction of its components through a series of chemical reactions. It is used in various ways: as a beverage, at festivals and even in religious rituals.

According to data released in 2017 by the International Organization of the Viticulture (OIV), global production is 246,700 hectoliters.

There are different types of wines, red, white or rosé, dry or sweet, depending on the sugar level, which are made by fermenting fruit.

The initiative to draw up a business plan for the production and commercialization of orange wine is to take advantage of the supply of exotic fruit that the country has at its disposal and bring a new product to the national market. The fruit that will be used to produce the wine is grown in the Ecuadorian Sierra. The competitive advantage is to take advantage of the raw materials that the country has and offer a different product to the consumer.

Nowadays, in the national and international markets, competitiveness is increasing, so the main challenge is to create a differentiated product with added value that allows and helps the country to be more productive in the agro-industrial sector. It is for this reason that conducting this study allows the introduction of new production technologies, to obtain a product of pleasant taste and excellent benefits, using this opportunity as a business and innovative alternative.

One of the main advantages of these products is that they will be manufactured to quality standards and will be affordable to everyone.

CHAPTER 1

1. PROBLEM

1.1 PROBLEM STATEMENT

According to 2017 data from the Central Bank of Ecuador, wine consumption in Ecuador is 70% imported wines and the remaining 30% domestically produced wines.

The taste for this drink allowed the spread of different wine varietals among Ecuadorians, so restaurants specializing in selling this type of product were opened.

Ecuador, specifically the Sierra region, grows traditional fruits such as oranges that are mostly underutilized, so there is an opportunity to grow the business by creating different products to meet consumer demands.

The demands of consumers at national and international level, as well as products made in accordance with quality and food safety standards, allow us to offer products that are beneficial for their consumption and meet their needs.

Through this study, we have identified a business opportunity in the Ecuadorian wine market, and therefore we intend to produce national wines for sale throughout the country, using a business plan that will allow us to enter the market and position the brand as an exotic beverage among consumers, obtaining economic benefits that will allow us to grow in the local and national wine market.

1.1.1 Diagnosis of the current situation

Diagnosis of the current wine situation in the country revealed the following reasons:

- **Nationally, there are few wine producers.**
  There are two national wine companies in the country that are recognized for the quality of the product they offer, Chaupi Estancia Winery, located in the province of Pichincha, and Bodegas Dos Henisferios, located in the province of Guayas, but wine production by these organizations is limited due to the limited cultivation of grapes.
- **Strengthening the positioning of imported wines in the market.**
  In supermarkets in Ecuador, you can find several types of wines brought from different countries that are already positioned by their brand. Due to the high quality of the product, we have wines from Chile, Argentina, Spain, USA, Canada, Italy, France and other countries.
- **There are no different flavors of wine in the domestic market.**
  Due to the lack of knowledge of producers for industrial fruit processing and wine production with different flavors.

1.1.2 Forecast: Effects

The assessment of the diagnosis of the current situation of wine consumption in the country has revealed possible consequences that may arise in the future.

the future.

- **Increase in the number of foreign wines in the domestic market.**
  Given the scarce production of national wines in the country, the consequence will be an increase in imports, so international brands continue to lead the national market.
- **Domestic wine production will show minimal growth.**
  As domestic supermarkets will continue to import foreign wines, the popularity of international brands will increase, leading to a reduction in wine production in the country.
- **Consumption of one serving of wine.**
  Foreign wines will continue to be imported, and national raw materials will not get the opportunity to undergo industrial processing and turn into a finished product.

1.1.3 Forecast control: possible solutions

- **Introduce a new product to the national market and determine if it will be accepted by the end user through market analysis.**
  Identifying a market niche will allow us to create a product with a different flavor and increase national production, offering a quality product that can compete with national and international brands.
- **Produce quality wine and develop marketing strategies to position it in the marketplace.**
  By developing marketing strategies, it is possible to create a competitive product in the market and in the same way increase customer loyalty.
- **Educating the public about the consumption of traditional fruit wines.**
  Implement promotional strategies to tell the public about the benefits of wine through talks, conferences, etc.

In addition, writing a business plan is very important because it allows you to think through the creation of the company with market research, marketing plan, technical study, administrative study and appropriate financial justification to make sure that the project is profitable.

1.2 PROBLEM DEFINITION

The present study was limited by the following framework:

1.2.1 Spatial delimitation

Units: Ecuador
Region: Sierra
Province: Bolívar
City: Kaluma
Location: 62 km southwest of Guaranda

9

Figure 1 Company location Source: *Google Maps*

1.2.2 Temporary demarcation

The information collected is based on statistics on wine imports over the last 5 years, ECB data, and on national orange production, MAGAP data.

The sources of texts on business plan development, financial feasibility, market research, and company formation requirements that are less than ten years old in relation to the year in which the research project is conducted were used for the study.

1.2.3 Universal delimitation

The population for which data had to be collected consists of the following groups:

- Guayaquil city residents who consume wine, according to a certain segment between 20 and 60 years old.

- Wine connoisseurs.

- Wine experts.

1.3 PROBLEM STATEMENT

(What would be the implications of developing a business plan for the production and marketing of orange wine?

1.4 PROBLEM SYSTEMATIZATION

How to conduct market research on orange wine production and sales?

What marketing strategies will be implemented to position the new product in the market?

(What financial, material and human resources are needed to set up such a project?

(How can the feasibility of the proposed venture be verified?

1.5 OBJECTIVES.

1.5.1 Overall objective
Development of a business plan for the production and commercialization of orange wine in the city of Guayaquil, using marketing and financial evaluation tools.

1.5.2 Specific objectives
1) To analyze the current situation of Wine Consumption, Production and Marketing in Poultry with the help of macro and micro environment analysis to know their competitors and establish themselves in the market.
2) Develop marketing strategies to position the product and increase customer loyalty in the national market.
3) Conduct a technical, administrative, and economic study to determine the resources needed to implement the project.
4) Prepare a financial justification to test the viability of the project. Project.

1.6 JUSTIFICATION

1.6.1 Theoretical justification
This research is based on theoretical knowledge bases such as: market research, which allows to know the segment targeted by the research project; technical research, which allows to know the technical characteristics of the product manufacturing process; marketing strategies, which help to promote the product and make the brand known in order to position itself in the market; administrative research, which determines the functions of the staff and the organizational structure of the organization; economic research and fi Thus, based on all this information, it is intended to make a business plan for the production and commercialization of orange wine and the promotion of national production in the country.

1.6.2 Methodological rationale
To achieve the objectives of the study we will use tools such as: SWOT analysis which allows us to analyze the micro and macro environment to create a strategy and better development of the organization; strategic planning allows us to create an organization structure that reflects the mission, vision, values and achieve the proposed goals; Michael Porter's competitive forces which helps to know in which sector the organization will compete.

To gather information, interviews will be conducted with consumers and experts who will share their experiences in the viral sector, and this research will be used to support this research project.

1.6.3 Practical justification
It is necessary to bring to the national market a product that is different from the wines offered on the market, thereby taking advantage of the raw materials available in the various sectors of the country, which are mostly unused, and thus try to stimulate national production, strengthen the country's economy, create jobs and contribute to the transformation of the production matrix.

Thus, with the help of tools to know the current market situation which helps to understand the segment in which the product will be introduced, the tastes of the customers, their characteristics and preferences and thus with the help of marketing strategies, it is possible to enter, promote and position the product in the national market in a competitive manner and create customer loyalty so that they feel satisfied with the product offered.

1.7 HYPOTHESIS

1.7.1 General hypothesis
The development of a business plan for the production and commercialization of orange wine in the city of Guayaquil will provide a beverage that is healthy for all consumers and will diversify its consumption.

1.7.2 Specific hypothesis
1) Analyzing the current situation of the wines existing in the country will analyze the macro and micro environment in order to know your competitors and strengthen yourself in the market.

2) Developing a marketing plan will help promote the product, position it in the market and build customer loyalty.
3) Conducting a technical, administrative and economic study will determine the resources needed to implement the project.
4) Performing a financial feasibility study will prove the profitability of the project.

1.8 OPERATIONALIZATION OF VARIABLES

Variables	Size	Subdimension	Indicators
BUSINESS PLAN FOR THE PRODUCTION AND MARKETING OF ORANGE WINE	Strategy	sector	• Macro- and micro-environmental analysis. • Competitive Forces. • SWOT.
	Market	Marketing plan Demand Suggestion	• 4 pp. • Segmentation. • Positioning. • Customer Loyalty. • Different aspects of buyers.
	Operational	Technical specifications	• Product Analysis. • Equipment and Techniques. • Distribution of the plant. • Control Systems.

Organization	Administrative	<ul><li>Executive Staff.</li><li>Organization.</li><li>Employees.</li><li>Supporting Organizations.</li></ul>
Economics and finance	Economic and financial indicators	<ul><li>Projected cash flow.</li><li>Profit and Loss Statement.</li><li>Comprehensive Project Assessment.</li><li>Recovery Period.</li><li>Balance Point.</li></ul>

Chapter 2

FRAME OF REFERENCE

2.1 RESEARCH HISTORY

2.1.1 History and origins of wine

Wine has a long history as its origin dates back to the beginning of mankind, the production of these drinks from the fermentation of grape juice was already established as early as 6,000 and 5,000 B.C. Archaeologists have discovered the rudiments of the first wine production, where the first cultivation of grapes occurred in the Bronze Age in places close to Sumeria and ancient Egypt.

The Egyptians fermented grape must or juice in large clay vessels and obtained red wine, and since then this product became a symbol of society, which was used in religious rituals and at any festivals.

Around 3000 BC, wine reached Western Europe and China via trade routes. Then in 700 BC, wine reached classical Greece, where the Greeks created containers of different sizes to store the product.

Later the production of this drink reached the Roman Empire in 200 B.C. It was introduced in Italy, the Romans planted vineyards all over Europe LKL.L with the different grape varieties that existed at that time, different types of wines were developed, where they also used wooden vats to transport the product. The Romans valued white wines the most, so they were stored in amphorae or wooden vats for 15-20 years to allow the product to mature.

During the Middle Ages, this drink was stored in wooden barrels in cellars, and the wine trade expanded and wine was displayed on the most exquisite tables and served on special occasions.

In modern times, in the early seventeenth and eighteenth centuries, wine was stored in glass bottles with a cork. Significant changes occurred with the advent of railroads, which began to be used as a means of transportation to bring the product to different parts of the region.

In 1927, several wine-producing countries joined together and formed an organization called the International Wine Office with the goal of producing products fit for human consumption with food standards and to avoid fraud in their production.

After the Second World War, in the 1960s and 1970s, the drink entered a golden age: new production technologies were developed, the drink experienced a new gastronomic boom, and it began to be consumed in restaurants. Over the years, wine has become a drink that is consumed all over the world by people from all walks of life.

Figure 2 Wine in Ancient Egypt
Source: (Abad, n.d.)

2.1.2 The concept of wine

INEN Standard (374) states that fruit wine is a beverage obtained by alcoholic fermentation of the must or juice of fresh fruit that undergoes the same procedure as grape wine.

According to (Maydata, 2002), a professor specializing in wine at Villa Clara University in Cuba defines wine as:

Wine is a beverage obtained from the alcoholic fermentation of grape juice, as well as other fruits and plant material. It is produced in three main stages: must production, fermentation and finally storage and aging (p. 135).

2.1.3 Wine classification

There are wines made to be consumed fresh (many whites, rosés, sparkling and young wines) that do not age well because they are made to be consumed within one year. But there are also those that are produced with the intention of aging for many years, both in barrels and in bottles (Barber, 2013).

Wines are categorized into:

According to their color:

- **Red wines:** The red color comes from the pigments in the grape skin. The longer the must is in contact with the skins, the more intense the color of the wine will be.
- **Rosé wines:** they are made from the same grapes as red wines, but the time between must and skins is much shorter.

- **White wines:** they are obtained by pressing white or black grapes. In the case of black grapes, it is necessary to prevent the must from staining, so the must and skins must be separated by sedimentation.

Figure 3 Wines by color
Source: (Barber, Viveros Barber, 2013)

According to their age:

- **Young wines:** these are wines that have not been aged in wood. Young wines are usually red, white or rosé.
- **Crianza wines: wines of** this type have spent some time between wood and bottle, they are characterized by their organoleptic characteristics.

Figure 4 Oak barrels, aged Source: (label, 2003)

Depending on the sugar content:

- **Dry wines:** these wines contain less than 5 grams of sugar per liter.

- **Abocado wines:** contain 15 to 30 grams of sugar per liter.

- **Semi-sweet wines:** contain 30 to 50 grams of sugar per liter.

Figure 5 Sweet sparkling wine
Source: (Smolec, 2017)

2.1.4 The process of making fruit wine

- **Receiving:** consists of quantifying the fruit to be used in the winemaking process. Suitable containers and calibrated equipment should be used at this stage.
- **Washing:** Fruit intended for processing should be washed to remove microorganisms and dirt residues. Chlorinated water should be used.
- **Culling:** Fruits that are not ripe for processing are culled.
- **Fruit preparation:** Peeling the fruit allows it to become softer and can be done mechanically or manually.
- **Pulp extraction:** carried out with a pulper or by liquefying the fruit.
- **Juice extraction:** the pulp from the previous step is passed through a sieve to extract the juice. The pulp must be kept at 70° C to prevent browning and guarantee flavor, color and aroma.
- **Wort preparation:** a solution of water with sugar and yeast and a nutrient, which can be ammonium phosphate, are added **to the** juice obtained in **the** previous step, after which pH, acidity and temperature are measured.
- **Fermentation:** At this stage, an air trap is placed to prevent oxidation to vinegar. Fermentation takes place in barrels for 5-10 days at a temperature not exceeding 30°C.
- **Transferring:** the process by which the fermented mixture is transferred from one container to another to remove fruit particles.
- **Filtration:** as in the previous step, the fermented mixture is passed through a fine cloth or sterilized sieve.
- **Pasteurization:** carried out to kill any remaining yeast.
- **Bottling:** This step is done in glass bottles, in the case of red wine in dark bottles and in the case of white wine in clear bottles.
- **Sealing:** done manually or mechanically, preferably with a cork plug.

2.1.5 The benefits of wine

Since ancient times, it has been attributed healing properties ranging from dietary to therapeutic. Among the main ones is its nutritional value, as it is considered a complete food, as well as a source of energy that is easily digested.

It is also associated with longevity as it contains vitamins A, C and several B-complex vitamins such as biotin, choline, encositol, cyancobalamin, folic acid, nicotinic acid, pyridoxine and thiamine among others. It contains a small amount of iron, so it is recommended for anemia. Useful properties of wine are due to the presence of tannins in it: the richer it is in tannins, the better it tones.

It also relieves anxiety and emotional tension. Due to its euphorizing properties, it is useful for depression. The salts contained in wine are perfectly absorbed: calcium, magnesium, silicon, zinc, fluorine, copper, manganese, chromium and sulfur mineral anion.

The polyphenols found in red wine give it antioxidant power that works against free radicals that contribute to premature tissue aging, damage in blood vessels, and the occurrence of certain cancers (Salazar, 2016).

2.2 THEORETICAL BASIS

2.2.1 Wine industry in Ecuador
The wine industry in the country developed in the fifties, Dr. Guillermo Serra, Don Sebastian Montaner and engineer Gaspar Serra decided to start a project to produce wines in Ecuador, thus founding the company "Union Vinicola International" in 1957, based in Miracle, where they produced their first products "Vinos Castell" and "Santa Cena", soon moved to Guayaquil, occupying various premises until they settled in their own factory.

In 1999, the winery Dos Hemisferios, located in Santa Elena, began by selling table grapes, but given the favorable characteristics of the soil and climate, they decided to devote themselves to wine production, obtaining great benefits and quality wines.

Winegrowing is constantly developing in Ecuador, so since 2002 there has been an organization called Cofriidin, created to promote the wine culture and with members in Guayaquil, Quito, Cuenca and Machala.

Three years later, in 2005, Ecuador held its first wine gala with national and international wines. This is one of the most important events for the virgin community, which for many years has promoted the culture of wine making, as well as giving recognition to national and foreign wines for their organoleptic properties.

In 2007, the II Wine Gala was held in Ecuador.

The III Ecuador Wine Gala and the I International Wine Competition were held in 2009.

The IV edition of the Wine Gala in Ecuador and the II International Wine Competition took place in 2011.

Today, the country also publishes Vimssimo, a wine magazine dedicated to cultural, social and educational aspects, so that both national and international consumers are informed about the steps the product is taking around the world.

Moises Aguiar and Andres Pazmino (2009), students of the Escuela Superior Politécnica de Litoral, argue in their research project that:

Montalvo, a canton in the province of Los Rios, produces wine from oranges, which is made in an artisanal way, resulting in a natural and organic wine. In addition, tropical fruits, especially oranges, have many aromatic compounds, which can be a new experience in the wine world. (page 12)

According to ZAMORA (2014), in his thesis project he describes the following:

In Ecuador, the fruit wine market is growing because there are companies that produce and sell fruit wines, but these products are made with chemicals that rob the wine of the purity and flavor that have always characterized it (p. 12).

Encalada, (2012) Wine expert who in the newspaper El Comercio states the following:

Another experience of artisanal wine production is registered in the district of Hima (Azuay). There they make wine from apples, but its production has not spread. The same happens in other towns in the country, such as Ambato and other areas of Tungurahua. This situation is due to the lack of support in promoting the product and because producers have to make investments to dedicate themselves to wine production. Among the alternative support options is the Caders program of the Ministry of Agriculture and Livestock, which covers 60% of the investment to start a micro-enterprise.

According to 2015 data from the Central Bank of Ecuador, 90% of the wine consumed is imported and the rest is produced by Ecuadorian companies, two of which are recognized for their exports internationally, these are Chaupi Estancia winery, located in the province of Pichincha, and Dos Hemisferios, located in the province of Guayas.

2.2.2 Different types of wines produced in Ecuador

The pins produce quality wines that compete with various imported brands such as various wines from Chile, Argentina, Spain, France, USA, Canada, Italy and other countries.

Among the most recognizable brands and companies in the pin industry:

Name of wine	Type of wine	Company	Location
PALOMINO FINE	White	ChaupiStay winery	Pichincha Province
PINO NOIR	Red	ChaupiStay winery	Pichincha Province
MERITAGE	Red	ChaupiStay winery	Pichincha Province
ALICE GREAT. RESERVE	Red	ChaupyStay winery	Pichincha Province
PARADOX	Red	Two hemispheres	Province of Guayas
BRUMA	Red	Two hemispheres	Province of Guayas
ENIGMA	White	Two hemispheres	Province of Guayas
DEL MORRO.	Red	Two hemispheres	Province of Guayas
TRAVESIA	Red	Two hemispheres	Province of Guayas

Table 1 Different types of wines produced in Ecuador

However, there are other wine companies that have a smaller market share, here are some of them

- Vinesa SA - Quito

- Tuscany - Cuenca

- Echeverria Machala-El Oro Winery

- Vino San Blas Quito

2.2.3 Types of wines imported into Ecuador

Between 60 and 70% of the wines on the Ecuadorian market are of Chilean origin, sold through the Mi Comisariato and Supermaxi supermarket chains; the remaining imported wines are of Argentine, Italian, French and other origins.

Brand of wine	Country of origin
Corte dei mori	Italy
Villa Maipo	Chile
Black cat	Chile
Southern Cone	Chile
Montes Reserves	Chile
Canepa	Chile
San Telmo	Argentina
Santa Julia Reserva	Argentina
St. Julian's	Argentina
Concha y Toro	Chile
Dona Paula	Argentina
Crocodile	Argentina
Chateau de Lamarque	France
Margot	France
Calvet Reserve	France

Table 2 Imported wines in the Ecuadorian market
Source: *Mana Fernanda Ladines and Diana Pineda, 2018*

2.2.4 Orange (Citrus X Sinensis)

Orange is an edible fruit derived from the sweet orange tree "Citrus x Sinensis" and the bitter orange tree "*Citrus Aurantium*". *These fruits grow best in moist environments.*

An orange can be described as a rounded fruit composed of segments and covered with a thick layer of oily peel that protects the inside from external influences (Bembibre, 2010).

(Herrera, 2012) Russ

Figure 6 Imported wines in the Ecuadorian market

oranges are known for their excellent health benefits and nutritional components.

Its nutritional composition is characterized by a low energy value due to its high water content and richness in vitamin C, folic acid and minerals such as potassium, magnesium and calcium. The latter is virtually unabsorbed by the body. It contains significant amounts of beta-carotene, which is responsible for its typical color and is known for its antioxidant properties, as well as malic, oxalic, tartaric and citric acids, the last of which enhances the effects of vitamin C. The amount of fiber is significant, which is found mainly in the white part between the pulp and the peel, so its consumption promotes intestinal transit.

2.2.5 Orange production in Ecuador

Ecuador is an agricultural country where different types of tropical fruits can be grown due to its wet or dry climate.

The low season of orange production in Ecuador starts in April, and the abundant harvest begins in July, August and September, so the price of oranges in the local market decreases.

According to the Ministry of Agriculture, Livestock, Aquaculture and Fisheries (MAGAP), in 2015, the national production of oranges increased from 114,308 tons to 116,809 tons, compared to 2014, 65.56% of production was concentrated in the province of Bolivar, in the canton of Caluma, and 60% of its inhabitants are involved in the cultivation of this fruit.

When there is a good crop year, harvesting continues through December, and when the production season ends, Ecuador imports the fruit.

2.2.6 Theoretical basis
What is a business plan?

A business plan is an organized document that describes the presentation or trajectory of a company or business and financial analysis from three perspectives: the past as its background, the current situation of the company and the forecast of goals and objectives, It should be noted that a business plan can be written to create a venture or improve the performance of an existing company, Weinberger (2009) states that a business plan can be written to create a venture or improve the performance of an existing company, Weinberger (2009):

A business plan is a document written in a clear, concise and simple form that is the result of a planning process. A business plan serves as a guide for a business because it shows all the steps, from the goals to be achieved to the day-to-day activities that will be designed to achieve them. The purpose of this document is to combine form and content. Form refers to the structure, wording and illustrations, how eye-catching it is, how "user-friendly" it is, while content refers to the plan as an investment proposal, the quality of the idea, financial information, analysis and market opportunities (p. 26).

The importance of preparing a business plan is to facilitate the analysis of competition, as Arias (2016) argues:

For a new company operating in a saturated market, it is important to know or identify what steps will help to reduce the number of failures in its first years and improve its adoption in the markets to which it is targeting its sales efforts, but how important is it to develop a business plan to establish a company, there is no doubt that neither;iyoii;i companies do not open their doors with a strategy already learned, but improvise as they go along, so it is worthwhile to make a comparison and conclude how important is it to develop a business plan and what is the difference between the two forms of (p.3)

2.2.7 Business Description

Companies are born from the creation or innovation of a product or service, the business description is based on the detailing of the products or services to be offered, thus (Guerrero, 1992).

The primary function of businesses has always been defined as making a profit. However, this is not their primary function. It can be said that the purpose of a company is to "CREATE CUSTOMERS", i.e. to identify customer needs and satisfy them.

2.2.8 Strategic business planning

In order to define the term strategic planning, it is necessary to review the concept of planning. Stoner, Freeman and Gilbert (2006) point out that planning involves the process of setting goals and selecting the means to achieve them (Ramirez, 2011).

Strategic planning is a consistent process that companies apply over many years to achieve their goals and objectives, promoting the best use of resources.

The main elements of strategic planning are:

- **Vision:** focuses on defining long-term goals, i.e. where the organization wants to go.

- **Mission:** defines the raison d'être of the organization, detailing why it exists and what it does to achieve the proposed vision.

- **Values:** these are the principles that guide the behavior of employees in an organization.

- **Strategies:** These are the actions to be taken to achieve the goal.

2.2.9 Components of a business plan
Market Analysis

Market analysis, according to Alvarez Luna and Ponce Garcia (2008), can be defined as:

Market research is simply necessary today, because no matter what activity an entrepreneur is going to engage in, it is necessary to know the target market, the motives and buying habits of its consumers, competitors' strategies and environmental trends. These elements allow the administration to make the right decisions to start its activities. Hence, it is important to use information of the required quality to make the right decisions. In many cases, wrong decisions are made due to misinterpretation of information or wrong predictions. But even though techniques such as market research are used to reduce risk in managerial decision making, managers are not exempted from applying their own experience, judgment and initiatives. Research provides certain data that reinforce opinion.

Market research or market analysis is a method that is used to collect data and use it, it serves entrepreneurs or traders to make decisions and meet the needs of consumers, thus Malhotra (2008) in his book defines market research as:

Market research involves identifying, collecting, analyzing, disseminating and using information. Each step in this process is important. A marketing research problem or opportunity is identified or defined and then the information needed to investigate it is determined. Since each marketing opportunity translates into a problem to be investigated, the terms "problem" and "opportunity" will be used interchangeably here. The sources of the required information are then identified and the usefulness of different data collection methods in terms of sophistication is evaluated. The most appropriate method is used to collect data, which is analyzed and interpreted, and then conclusions are drawn. Finally, conclusions, implications and recommendations are presented in a format that allows the information obtained to be used to make marketing decisions and act on them. (p. 8)

Technical analysis

The technical study of a project consists of formulating and analyzing the various technological initiatives to produce the proposed goods or services, which also verifies the technical feasibility of each process. This technical analysis identifies the equipment, machinery, raw materials and facilities that will be required to start the project and also answers the relevant questions of where, when, how much, how and by what means the desired things will be produced, so the technical or operational analysis of a project includes everything related to the functioning and operation of the new business or company.

In his book Evaluation financiera de proyectos (Orozco) he notes that:

A technical study is designed to verify the technical feasibility of producing a product or providing a service to achieve the project objectives. The main objective of this study is to determine whether it is possible to produce and sell the product or service with the required quality, quantity and cost; this requires the identification of technology, machinery, equipment, inputs, raw materials, processes, human resources, etc. The technical study must be coordinated with the market study, since production is carried out to meet the sales identified in the latter study. The technical study is carried out by experts in the target area of the investment project (engineers, technicians, architects, etc.) and proposes to identify technical alternatives to achieve the objectives of the project and is one of the stages of the pre-feasibility study that requires the most attention, since the entire financial architecture of the project, corresponding to the evaluation of investments, costs and revenues, is based on its results. (c. 26).

Administrative analysis

In the administrative analysis of a business plan, a human resource study is conducted, profiles of the people who will be part of it and the functions delegated to them, an organizational chart that represents the positions of the organization and their hierarchical levels.

Financial analysis

In his research article on economics and finance, Anzi (2016) concluded that:

A financial study is a fundamental part of evaluating an investment project. It may analyze a new venture, an existing organization, or a new investment by a company, such as the creation of a new line of business, the purchase of another company, or an investment in a new manufacturing facility.

2.2.10 SWOT analysis

SWOT analysis is defined as a tool to diagnose the internal and external situation of an organization and thus identify competitive strategies to improve its development.

Trejo Natalia, Trejo Elia, and Zuniga Honatan (2016) identify the views of the following authors in their journal:

According to Thompson and Strickland (1998), once a SWOT analysis has been conducted, it is possible to act directly on strengths and weaknesses (internal factors) because they are variables dependent on the organization. On the other hand, opportunities and threats are independent (external factors) and therefore difficult to change (p. 10).

2.2.11 Environmental analysis of pistils

KAREN AGUIRRE and JENNIFFER ALLAUCA (2016) in their research project define pestiferous analysis as:

PEST (Political, Economic, Social and Legal) analysis is a strategy tool used to examine a company's macro environment. Because they are outside the company's control, they should usually be viewed as threats or opportunities to be considered when planning and developing the business (p. 11).

2.2.12 Michael Porter's 5 forces

The 5 competitive forces method for companies aims to find out in which sector they compete, maximize their resources and generate value.

Porter, Five Competitive Forces (2008) In his book, he identifies the importance of conducting analysis to determine the intensity of competition and rivalry in an organization:

Understanding the structure of a sector is as important for investors as it is for managers. The five competitive forces show whether a sector is truly attractive and help investors anticipate positive or negative changes in sector structure before they become apparent. The five forces distinguish short-term problems from structural change and allow investors to capitalize on unwarranted pessimism or optimism. Those companies whose strategies have the potential to transform the sector become much more visible. This deep understanding of competition is a more powerful way to achieve true investment success than the financial forecasts and trend extrapolation that dominate investment analysis today.

2.2.12.1 Porter's 5-power model.

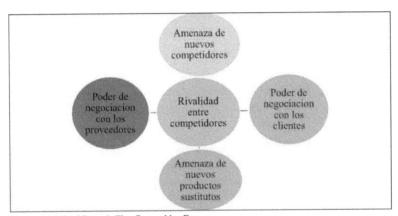

Figure 7 Michael Porter's Five Competitive Forces
Source: Mana Fernanda Ladines and Diana Pineda, 2018

Rivalry between competitors

Rivalry between existing competitors in a particular sector arises because competitors feel the impact on improvement, organizations are very dependent on market acceptance, so to compete they use pricing tactics, discounts, advertising, introduction of new products etc.

Threat of new competitors

The creation of new enterprises generates a desire to capture a larger market share, which can force existing enterprises to reduce production costs and selling prices.

The main concept that needs to be analyzed at this stage is the constraints and barriers to entry that prevent the flow of revenue from one organization to another. According to (Porter, Five competitive forces, 2008) "Barriers to entry are the advantages that established players have over new entrants". Some barriers to entry are as follows.

- **Economies of scale:** It is based on increasing production volume to reduce costs.

- **Product differentiation:** it is the addition of value to a product to attract customer attention and achieve brand positioning.
- **Capital investment: the** financing of economic resources to improve the processes of an organization and generate economic benefits.
- **Access to sales channels:** it's about improving relationships with customers, offering low prices to expand existing demand.
- **Public policy: a** country's public policy may prevent new competitors from entering the market.

Negotiations with clients

Effective buyers can benefit more if they force prices down. They succeed if they have bargaining power, especially if they use that power to drive prices down.

Negotiations with suppliers

Powerful suppliers capture a larger share of value by charging higher prices. A market or market segment will not be attractive if the suppliers are well organized and can impose their price levels. The situation will be more serious for the organization if the products offered by these suppliers have no substitutes.

Threat of new substitute products

Organizations face serious challenges when new products enter the market. If a substitute product fulfills the same need, the situation is more complicated if these products are developed with new technologies and can be offered at lower prices.

2.2.13 Marketing plan

A marketing plan focuses on meeting customer needs, describing the type of product to be offered, setting prices, identifying the target market and how to promote the product.

"Marketing is about managing profitable customer relationships. The twin goals of marketing are to attract new customers by promising them superior value and to retain and increase existing customers by meeting their needs." (PHILIP Kotler and GARY Armstrong, 2012)

2.2.14 The 4 P's of the marketing mix

Marketing mix is a product planning process for which there are 4 main variables.

Figure 8 4 P marketing mix
Source: Mana Fernanda Ladines and Diana Pineda, 2018

Product: the means by which consumer needs are met. It is based on product attributes, benefits, logo.

Price: it focuses directly on establishing pricing strategies that meet consumer demands, price helps to position the product.

Distribution: it is the activity of transporting products to various points of sale, along the most advantageous routes.

Promotion: it is based on the communication strategies used by organizations to sell the product.

2.3 CONCEPTUAL FRAMEWORK

Quality: Quality describes the ability of an object to satisfy the required needs according to some parameter, fulfillment of quality requirements.

Cultivation: Cultivation is the experience of spreading seeds in the soil and doing the necessary work to produce fruit from them.

Manufacturing: Obtaining a product through the sequential transformation of one or more materials.

Entrepreneurship: the initiation of an activity that requires effort or work to produce a favorable result.

Strategy: a strategy is a procedure that defines a series of steps to achieve a certain goal.

Fermentation: Fermentation is a natural process that occurs in certain compounds or elements by the action of various actors and can be simplified as a process of incomplete oxidation (Bembibre, ABC Definition, 2010).

Market: a public place with stores or stalls where people trade, especially food and other consumer goods.

27

Must: The result of extracting juice from fruit to produce wine.

Polyphenols: a group of chemicals **found** in plants.

Production: Production is any activity aimed at making, processing or obtaining goods and services (DefinicionMX, 2017).

2.4 CONTEXTUAL FRAMEWORK

The research project is limited to the province of Bolívar, the city of Caluma, where no studies have been conducted on this topic, so the theses of several authors who have carried out fruit wine projects are described.

(Melero, 2009) in his doctoral thesis states that several technologies have been studied to improve the production of red wines in hot climate areas to improve the color and aromatic fraction of wines. Of all of them, ion exchange treatment seems to be very interesting for improving color and cold maceration for increasing the polyphenol and aroma content of wines. (page 5)

(Zurita, 2011) in his research project states that to utilize the non-commodity fruit obtained from the post-harvest process in AGRICOLA PITACAVA which produces and exports pitahaya fruit, the quantity is 200 kg per harvest and this quantity is enough to produce fruit wine, In concentration with carambola, this will help to increase the vitamin C content of the product to achieve better preservation of the fruit wine and thus help AGRICOLA PITACAVA to get the added value of the non-commodity fruit. (p.14)

(Remache, 2015) in his research project states that fermented orange beverage produced by artisanal method is a serious problem of turbidity giving a poor appearance to the final product as a result of poor clarification, hence the need to test and establish methods of sediment stability at the clarification stage. (page 21)

(Rodnguez, 2016) in his research project states that due to the background of this study, the aim is to develop a Mango wine based on two mango varieties Ataulfo and Tommy Hatkins, evaluating their characteristics.

Hycochemical and organoleptic tests after application of three different yeast concentrations (page 18).

2.5 LEGAL FRAMEWORK

2.5.1 Constitution of the Republic of Ecuador 2008.

2.5.2 Organic Production Code

2.5.3 National Plan "For a decent life" for 2013-2017

2.5.4 Resolucion ARCSA-DE-057-2015-GGG

2.5.5 RESOLUCION ARCSA-DE-067-2015-GGG

2.5.6 Norma Tecnica Ecuatoriana NTE INEN 374 - 2015 Alcoholic beverages. Fruit wine.

Physico-chemical requirements in accordance with INEN 374 - 2015

Requirements	Unit	Mimmo	Maximo	Method Essay
Alcohol, volume fraction	%	5.0	18,0	Inen 360.
Volatile acid	G/L	-	1.5	Inen 341

acetic acid				
Volatile acid in the form of butyric acid	g/l	4.0	16,0	INEN 347.
Methanol	*	-	0,5	INEN 348.
Ashes	mEq/L	1,4	-	INEN 547.
Alkalinity ash	g/l		-	INEN 353.
Chlorides in the form of sodium chloride	g/l	-	2,0	INEN 354.
Glycerin	*	1	10,0	INEN 355.
anhydride total sulfur	g/l	-	0,32	INEN 356.
anhydride free sulfur	g/l	-	0,4	INEN 357.

Table 3 Physico-chemical requirements according to the Inen standard
Source: INEN Standard 374 - 2015

2.5.7 Ecuadorian technical standard NTE INEN 1334-1- 2015

2.5.8 Operating permit

National Agency for Regulation, Control and Supervision in the Health Care Sphere

Chapter 3

3.1 COMPANY PRESENTATION

"VINOS DEL PACIFICO S.A.". It is a private company that produces and sells orange wine in the city of Guayaquil, a directly Ecuadorian product.

This company is located in the canton of Caluma, province of Bolivar, the environment of this canton is beautiful as it is surrounded by hills, mountains and especially the cultivation of oranges, which is completely natural, a good opportunity for agro-industrial development in this sector.

"VINOS DEL PACIFICO S.A"

Figure 9   Company logo
Source: Mara Fernanda Ladines and Diana Pineda, 2018

3.1.1 Mission

"VINOS DEL PACIFICO S.A. is dedicated to the production and marketing of wines that provide satisfaction and loyalty through their exquisite taste. We are committed to producing wines of the highest quality to achieve our brand positioning in the local, national and international markets, contributing to the economic development of the country.

9.1.2 Vision

In the next 5 years, to become the leading company in the production and sale of orange wines, developing important strategic alliances, constantly innovating and adapting to new market trends and the needs of our customers.

9.1.3 Values

"VINOS DEL PACIFICO S.A." strives to be an organization based on:

- **Authenticity:** to be true to our customers, all of our innovations must reflect the essence of who we are and where we come from.
- **Quality:** We implement effective quality management in accordance with established processes, and everything we do in every relationship with the customer, employees, workers and suppliers is optimally effective.
- **Respect**: for the traditional methods that started wine and the representation it has

in our culture.
- **Teamwork**: We want all employees to be committed and give their best by working as a team.

9.1.4 Product Presentation

The orange wine "Vino Caluma" will be created through a natural fermentation process. This drink has many benefits such as: prevents disease, gives energy, reduces fats, contains vitamins A and C, helps control emotional anxiety, reduces fats, reduces the risk of heart attack.

The final product retains the properties and numerous health benefits due to its origin, where orange is the raw material for this product. This product is based on meeting the needs of people consuming natural products that quench thirst, that can be enjoyed at any meal and above all, that are good for the health of consumers. However, there are many opportunities to produce this kind of products, as we have an abundance of fruits, different flavors and aromas that allow us to create different and healthy products. For this project, the safety of the product will be taken into consideration as well as all the regulations that help to support the product.

Orange wine will pair well with red meats, savory dishes with the sweetness and acidity of this fruit, and sweet dishes with the sour-sweet flavor of orange.

This type of drink can also be used as an ingredient in the preparation of some gastronomic dishes.

Figura 10   Product Presentation, Caluma Wine
Source: Mana Fernanda Ladines and Diana Pineda, 2018

3.2 MARKET ANALYSIS

In order to identify opportunities to produce and sell orange wine in the city of Guayaquil, market research will be conducted through surveys to characterize the product, as well as interviews with consumers and producers who are experts in wine to determine their perceptions in a more open way.

The goal of this project is to bring the product to the alcoholic beverage market, especially the Ecuadorian market, satisfying an unmet need of the consumer.

3.2.1 Analysis of sectors and companies

The market analysis will focus on the entire community of the city of Guayaquil, which is home to 2'644,891 people made up of men and women, according to 2017 Inec data.

The Ecuadorian market currently accounts for more than 70% of imported wines, resulting in 30% of national production, among the main national competitors in the Ecuadorian wine market are: Vinos Dos Hemisferios, located in the province of Guayas and the company Chaupi Estanca Winery, located in the province of Pichincha, in addition, there is also very strong competition from imported wines from Chile, Argentina, Italy, Spain, Canada, France and others. For this reason, there is a proposal to bring to the market a new product that will be produced from national raw materials and will have advantages and organoleptic properties.

To further explore the market, Michael Porter's 5 competitive forces were analyzed and are detailed below.

1. Rivalry between competitors.

VINOS DEL PACIFICO S.A." has two competitors in the country: Chaupi Estancia, located in the province of Pichincha, and Dos Hemisferios, located in Guayaquil. The two major competitors existing in the market form a monopoly on wine production in the country.

CALUMA wines can directly compete with these two companies because they offer variety in their products, having a wide variety of wines already on the market.

Our competitors are characterized by promoting their products in different ways each year, be it price, advertising, etc.

2. The threat of new competitors.

There is a possibility that a new wine company will enter the market offering different flavors, as the country grows different fruits with many health benefits, and at the same time a strategic alliance between two companies that are currently competing with each other may emerge and import a brand that will directly compete with CALUMA wine.

The creation and experience of VINOS DEL PACIFICO S.A. is not in comparison with the companies that currently exist in the country; because these companies are already known and have an already positioned market segment. Therefore, these companies produce and sell their products on a large scale, while our company will start its operations in the national market (Guayaquil city).

3. The threat of substitute products.

Wine is a very important part of gastronomic culture and eating habits. In this industry, new competitors are constantly emerging with substitute products in the beverage sector, allowing the creation of strategies that help not to influence the price of wines and the implementation of marketing strategies that help to recognize the product with greater strength, knowing that wine satisfies needs that can be covered by other products.

4. The bargaining power of suppliers.

The main suppliers in the wine sector are growers, collectors and primary processors who will help to provide raw materials for warehouses. Our company has suppliers in the town of Bolivar, Canton of Calumet. The more suppliers we have, the more bargaining power we have with them, as they will not be able to easily increase their prices. The bargaining power of suppliers allows us to develop strategies to reach agreements with suppliers or, in any case, to analyze strategies that allow us to have more control over them.

5. The bargaining power of consumers.

The purpose of this item is to examine the degree of influence that consumers or customers have on suppliers. VINO DEL PACIFICO S.A. does not yet stand out among the competitors on the market, as these companies offer a quality product and a fair price for the different types of wine they offer. Our customers are: supermarkets, stores and small businesses (restaurants, bars). In supermarkets we can bargain with 0 because we have a lot of competition and variety of products. However, in stores and small businesses the bargaining power is great because they can buy our product at the price we set.

3.2.2 Analyze the market appropriately

The market as a whole in the city of Guayaquil consists of Guayaquil residents, people between 20 and 60 years old, divided into men and women, so it was proposed to conduct a study through surveys to determine the supply and demand for the product; and to determine the feasibility of the project.

Studies have shown that drinking certain types of wine has a strong impact on people's lifestyles.

Supply Analysis: Supply is what attracts buyers, what they are willing to pay for. During the study, it was found that there are various types of wines, both domestic and imported, but there is no domestically produced orange flavored wine in the market.

Demand Analysis: Through surveys and interviews it can be determined how customers will visit the store in the future, what will be the supply i.e. the number of products that will be produced to meet this demand, the demand actually depends on factors such as: price, the need that the customer requires from the product and also the taste.

Pablo Taramelli, owner of Dos Hemisferios, says that in the last 10 years, wine consumption per person in Ecuador has increased from one glass to one bottle. The highest consumption is in Quito, Guayaquil and Cuenca, so that in 2014 the demand for wine was 300,000 bottles and by 2020 it is estimated that production will increase to 600,000.

3.2.3 Target market

For this market research, the number of inhabitants of the city of Guayaquil as the target market segment was taken as a basis, according to the statistics of the INEC forecast in 2017, the city of Guayaquil has 2'644.891 inhabitants, composed of men and women, of which it was decided to take as target population people between 20 and 60 years old who study, work or have a criterion formed for the consumption of this type of alcoholic beverage, the population to be studied is 1'192.201 inhabitants.

age category	population 2010 guayaquil
20 to 24 years old	201.942
25 - 29 years old	192.971
30 - 34 years old	182.010
35 to 39 years old	156.986
40 - 44 years old	138.361
45-49 years old	128.431
50 to 54 years old	104.761
55 - 60 years old	86.739
total	1'192.201

Table 4 Residents of the City of Guayaquil by age group
Source: 2010 Population Census - INEC

3.2.4 Population and sampling

To determine the population and sample size, we draw from the target market, which, as stated in the previous chapter, is 1'192,201 people.

Simple random sampling will be done by age group, people between 20 and 60 years old.

For this study, it was decided to work with a confidence level of 95% and a margin of error of 0.05%.
The Z-table determined that the 95 percent confidence probability is 1.96.
-- The probability of success will be 50%, which corresponds to accepting the

product and the remaining 50% is the probability of failure, people who decide to

buying from the competition.

35

Infinite Population (Unknown)

Where:

N: Sample size, total number of people to be interviewed

Z: 95% confidence level equivalent to 1.96

P: Probability of success, product acceptance, equivalent to 50%.

Q: A probability of failure equivalent to 50%.

E: error limit equivalent to 0.05%.

3.2.5 Population Calculation:

$$n: = \frac{z^2(p*q)}{e^2}$$

$$n: = \frac{1.96^2(0.5*0.5)}{0,05^2}$$

$$n: = \frac{3.84(0.25)}{0.0025}$$

$$n: 400$$

The sample size for the survey is 400 people, residents of the city of Guayaquil between the ages of 20 and 60.

3.2.6 Analysis and interpretation of results

Surveys were conducted in different neighborhoods of the city such as Urdesa, Saukes, Samanes, 9 de October, as well as in Salvador Allende's University District, Delta Avenue and Kennedy Avenue.

Genre

genre	frequency	percentage	total interest
Woman	235	59%	59%

Man	165	41%	100%
Total		100%	

Table 5 Gender of the surveyed population
Source: Metric! Fernanda Ladines and Diana Pineda, 2018

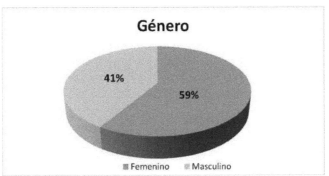

Figure 11 Gender affiliation of the surveyed population
Source: Maria Fernanda Ladines and Diana Pineda, 2018

Analysis

To study the wine market in the city of Guayaquil, 400 people were interviewed, of which, according to the results obtained, 235 were women, representing 59%, and 165 were men, representing 41%.

dad

age	frequency	percentage	percentage accumulated
29-38	202	50%	50%
39-48		18%	68%
18-28	70	18%	86%
49-60	55	14%	100%
Total		100%	

Table 6 Age of the surveyed population
Source: Mana Fernanda Ladines and Diana Pineda, 2018

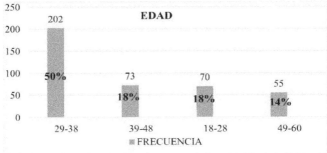

Figure 12 Age of the surveyed population

Source: Mana Fernanda Ladines and Diana Pineda, 2018

Analysis

400 people were surveyed in different neighborhoods of Guayaquil city, the age groups were divided in order to find out which of the population of a given age range consumes more wine. The most significant range is between 29 and 38 years old, divided between male and female, which represents 50%, the next age range is between 39 and 48 years old, which represents 18%, followed by the range between 18 and 28 years old, which also represents 18% and finally 14% for the age range between 49 and 60 years old.

1. ^What beverages do you consume?

unique type of drink Are you consuming?	frequency	percentage	total interest
Whiskey	90	22%	22%
Beer	110	28%	50%
Wine	80	20%	
Vodka	80	20%	90%
Ron	40	10%	100%
Total		100%	

Table 7 Type of beverage consumed
Source: Mana Fernanda Ladines and Diana Pineda, 2018

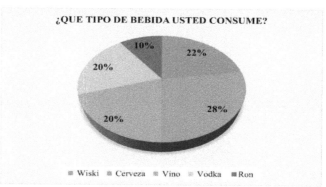

¿QUE TIPO DE BEBIDA USTED CONSUME?

Wiski Cerveza Vino Vodka Ron

Figure 13 Type of beverage consumed
Source: Mana Fernanda Ladines and Diana Pineda, 2018

Analysis

According to surveys on beverage consumption in the city of Guayaquil, 28%

consume beer, followed by 22% whiskey, 20% vodka and wine and finally 10% rum.

2. What kind of wine do you drink?

What kind of wine do you drink?	Frequency	Percentage	Cumulative percentage
Peach	95	24%	24%
Grapes	170	42%	66%
Orange	90	23%	89%
Apple	45	11%	100%
Total		100%	

Table 8 Taste of the wine you consume
Source: Maria Fernanda Ladines and Diana Pineda, 2018

Figure 14 The flavor of the wine you consume
Source: Maria Fernanda Ladines and Diana Pineda, 2018

Analysis

42% of respondents prefer grape wine, 24% prefer peach wine, 23% prefer orange wine and finally 11% prefer apple wine.

3. How often do you consume wine?

HOW OFTEN DO you drink wine?	Frequency	Percentage	Cumulative percentage
Daily		13%	13%
1 or 2 times a week			32%
Every 15 days	82	21%	53%
once a month	189	47%	100%
Total		100%	

Table 9 How often you drink wine

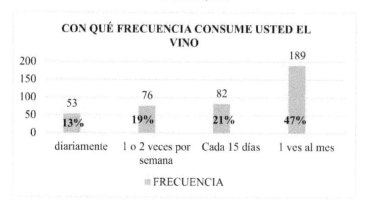

Figure 15 How often do you consume wine?
Source: Mana Fernanda Ladines and Diana Pineda, 2018

Analysis

According to the results of the analysis, it can be determined that most of the people surveyed consume wine at least once a month, which corresponds to 47%, followed by consumption every 15 days, which represents 21% of the respondents, followed by consumption once or twice a week, which represents 19%, and finally daily consumption, which represents 13%.

4. What wine do you consume most often?

What wine do you consume most often?	Frequency	Percentage	Percentage Accumulated
White			
Pink	92	23%	42%
Red	190	48%	90%
Sparkling wines	40	10%	100%
Total		100%	

Table 10 Which wine do you drink most often?
Source: Mana Fernanda Ladines and Diana Pineda, 2018

¿QUE TIPO DE VINO CONSUME CON MÁS
FRECUENCIA?

Espumosos 10%, Blanco 19%, Tinto 48%, Rosado 23%

■ Blanco ■ Rosado ■ Tinto ■ Espumosos

Figure 16 Which wine do you drink most often?
Source: Mana Fernanda Ladines and Diana Pineda, 2018

Analysis:

The analysis of this question showed that the majority of respondents prefer to drink red wine - 48%, followed by rose wine - 23%, white wine - 19% and finally sparkling wine - 10%.

EN QUÉ LUGAR USTED COMPRA EL VINO

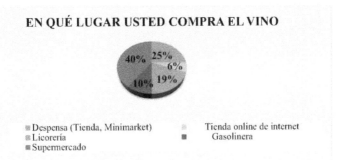

40% 25% 6% 10% 19%

■ Despensa (Tienda, Minimarket)   ■ Tienda online de internet
■ Licorería   ■ Gasolinera
■ Supermercado

5. Where do you buy this product?

Where do you buy your wine?	Frequency	Percentage	Cumulative percentage
Pantry (store, minimarket)	100	25%	25%
Online internet store	25	6%	31%
Licoreria	75		50%
gas station	40	10%	60%
Supermarket	160		100%
Total		100%	

Table 11 Where do you buy wine
Source: Mana Fernanda Ladines and Diana Pineda, 2018

Figura 17   The place where you buy wine

Analysis:

Surveys show that most people buy this product from supermarkets 40%, then 25% of people buy this product from grocery stores, convenience stores or minimarts, 19% of people buy this product from liquor stores, 10% of people buy it from gas stations and finally 6% of people buy this product online.

6. for what occasions do you use this product?

For what occasions do you use this product?	Frequency	Percentage	Cumulative percentage
Special cases	170	42%	42%
Meetings (Home)	40	10%	52%
Birthdays		30%	82%
Meals (lunch - dinner)		15%	97%
Others	10	3%	100%
Total		100%	

Table 12 The occasions for which you drink wine
Source: Mana Fernanda Ladines and Diana Pineda, 2018

Figura 18   The occasions for which you consume wine
Source: Mana Fernanda Ladines and Diana Pineda, 2018

Analysis:

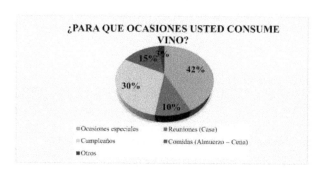

From the results of the analysis we can determine that most of the respondents consume this product on special occasions which is 42%, followed by 30% of people who consume it on birthdays, then 10% who consume it in meetings or at home, 5% of people consume it during meals, lunches or dinners and finally 3% of the respondents consume this drink for any other reason.

7. What is the most important factor for you when choosing a good wine?

Please indicate the factor that is most important to you when choosing a good wine.	Frequency	Percentage	Percentage Accumulated
Price	30	7%	7%
Quality	75		26%
Flavor	150	37%	63%
Design/presentation		4%	67%
Brand	70	17%	84%
Not far from the place of sale/sales	10	3%	87%
Origin of the pins	50	13%	100%
Total		100%	

Table 13 Important factor when choosing a wine
Source: Mana Fernanda Ladines and Diana Pineda, 2018

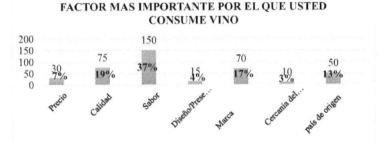

Figura 19   An important factor when choosing a wine
Source: Mana Fernanda Ladines and Diana Pineda, 2018
Analysis:

According to the analysis, 37% of people surveyed consume wine because of its taste, followed by 19% of people consume it because of the quality of the product, then 13% of people consume it because of the brand, 13% because of the country of origin, 7% because of price, 4% because of design and presentation and finally 3% because of proximity to the place of sale.

8. From which country did you consume wine?

J) In what country have you consumed wine?	Frequency	Percentage	Cumulative percentage
Argentina	107	27%	27%
Chile	160		67%
Ecuador	93	23%	90%
France	40	10%	100%
Total		100%	

Table 14 From which country you consumed wine
Source: Mana Fernanda Ladines and Diana Pineda, 2018

Figura 20   What country did you use the wine from
Source: Mana Fernanda Ladines and Diana Pineda, 2018

Analysis

According to the analysis of the people surveyed, 40% said they consumed wines of Chilean origin, followed by 27% of Argentinian wines, 23% of Ecuadorian wines and finally 10% of French wines.

9. How much have you ever paid for wine?

How much have you ever paid for wine?	Frequency	Percentage	Percentage Accumulated
$5-$10	50	12%	12%
$10-15		11%	23%
$15-$20	170	43%	66%
$20-$30	136	34%	100%
Total		100%	

Table 15 Maximum amount you can pay for wine
Source: Mana Fernanda Ladines and Diana Pineda, 2018

Figura 21   The maximum you can pay for wine

Analysis:

According to the surveys, 43% of people indicated they paid $15 to $20 for wine, followed by 34% of people indicating they paid $20 to $30, 12% paid $5 to $10 and 11% of people paid $10 to $15 for wine.

10. What is your monthly income?

What is your monthly income?	Frequency	Percentage	Cumulative percentage
Base salary		15%	15%
400 - 600	110	27%	42%
600 - 800	160		82%
800 or more	70	18%	100%
Total		100%	

Table 16 Monthly income
Source: Source: Mana Fernanda Ladines and Diana Pineda, 2018

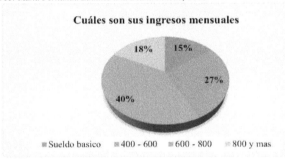

Cuáles son sus ingresos mensuales

18%   15%
27%
40%

▪ Sueldo basico   ▪ 400 - 600   ▪ 600 - 800   ▪ 800 y mas

Figure 22 Monthly income
Source: Mana Fernanda Ladines and Diana Pineda, 2018

Analysis:

Forty percent of respondents indicated their monthly income was between $600 and *$700,* followed by 27% with incomes between $400 and $600, 18% with incomes between $400 and $600, and 18% with incomes between $600 and $600.
800 dollars and above and finally 15% of people who receive a base salary as their monthly income.

11. Do you know the health benefits of wine?

Do you know about the health benefits of wine?	Frequency	Percentage	Percentage Accumulated
Yes	304	76%	76%
No		24%	100%

Total		100%

Table 17 Knowledge about the benefits of wine
Source: Mana Fernanda Ladines and Diana Pineda, 2018

Figura 23   Knowledge of the benefits of wine
Source: Mana Fernanda Ladines and Diana Pineda, 2018

Analysis

From the 400 people surveyed, it is clear that 76% of people are aware of the

about the benefits of wine, while 24% of people said they did not know about the
benefits of wine.

12. What kind of presentation would you like to see in wine?

What kind of presentation would you like to see in a wine?	Frequency	Percentage	Cumulative percentage
Glass container.	230	57%	57%
Tetra Park		30%	87%
Biodegradable packaging	40	10%	97%
Plastic container	10	3%	100%
Total		100%	

Table 18 Presentation of wine
Source: Mana Fernanda Ladines and Diana Pineda, 2018

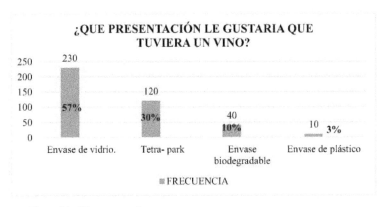

Figura 24   Wine presentation
Source: Mana Fernanda Ladines and Diana Pineda, 2018

Analysis

According to the survey, 230 people prefer glass presentations, which is 57%, followed by 30% who prefer tetra-park presentations, 10% who prefer biodegradable containers, and 3% who prefer plastic containers.

13. Are you ready to consume orange wine produced in Ecuador?

Would you be willing to drink orange wine produced in Ecuador?	Frequency	Percentage	Cumulative percentage
Yes	298	74%	74%
No	102	26%	100%
Total		100%	

Table 19 Acceptability level of orange wine
Source: Mana Fernanda Ladines and Diana Pineda, 2018

ARE YOU READY TO CONSUME ORANGE WINE PRODUCED IN ECUADOR?

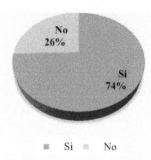

Figure 25 Acceptability level of orange wine
Source: Mana Fernanda Ladines and Diana Pineda, 2018

Analysis

According to surveys conducted in the city of Guayaquil, 74% of people said that the
whether they would be willing to drink orange wine, while 26% of people responded that they would not drink orange wine.

How much would you be willing to pay for 750ml of orange wine?

How much would you be willing to pay for 750ml of orange wine?	Frequency	Percentage	Cumulative percentage
$ 5 - $10	58	15%	15%
$10 - $15	204	51%	66%
$15 - $20		24%	90%
$20-$30		10%	100%
Total		100%	

Table 20 How much would you be willing to pay for a 750 ml orange wine
Source: Maria Fernanda Ladines and Diana Pineda, 2018

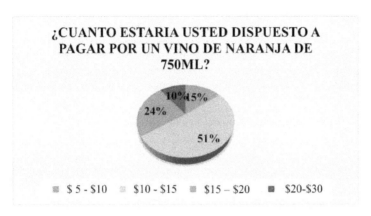

¿CUANTO ESTARIA USTED DISPUESTO A PAGAR POR UN VINO DE NARANJA DE 750ML?

- $ 5 - $10
- $10 - $15
- $15 – $20
- $20-$30

Figure 26 How much would you be willing to pay for 750 ml of orange wine?
Source: Maria Fernanda Ladines and Diana Pineda, 2018

Analysis:

According to the polls, 51% of people said they would be willing to pay $10 to $15 for this drink, then 24% of people said they would pay $15 to $20, 15% of people would be willing to pay $5 to $10 and finally 10% of people would pay $20 to $30.

3.2.7 Interviews with experts in the field of viral culture

1. Name of interviewee: Nestor Mosquera

Interviewee's profession: commercial engineer, export assistant at Pro Ecuador.

Duration of the interview: 25 minutes

Do you believe the growth of Virncola production has been constant over time?

Globally, the growth of alcoholic beverages has increased in recent years due to the fact that society is gradually becoming more cultured in its consumption of beverages and due to the emergence of restaurants that are just as concerned about the distribution of this alcohol.

Is there an advantage in the wine market?

There is no advantage in the wine market due to excessive competition from drinks such as beer, whiskey, rum, tequila, but with a good image and advertising it is possible to promote this drink and compete directly with the leading companies in sales.

In terms of substitutes, what are the most competitive products that can replace wine?

As mentioned, wines are in direct competition with fermented spirits such as beer, whiskey and, as lower alcohol content drinks, cocktails, sangas and others.

What do you think is the best strategy for entering the market with a new product

like orange wine?

The best strategy is to look directly for a market niche to offer, focus on it, stimulate consumption, talk about the benefits this drink has and how it is directly developed, set affordable prices for a segmented market and finally promote well, as any new product in the market depends solely on the advertising and the offer to be made to it.

How technologically challenging is it to start a wine company?

The equipment to be used for wine production in terms of distillation, fermentation and bottling is easy to learn and operate, but the investment in it is complex, given that opening a wine production facility requires a minimum investment of $150,000 for equipment to match its production level.

Do you recommend producing orange wine?

Orange wine is essentially a fruit wine and when considered from the point of view of obtaining raw materials, it is readily available and good market research, technical and physico-chemical study of the product will ensure feasibility over a period of time.

Is there any state support for the development of domestic winemaking?

Changing the production matrix is a government incentive that directly supports national production, in addition, there are also government organizations that support the financing of investments of established companies.

What would you recommend for the production and commercialization of orange wine in the Ecuadorian market?

As mentioned earlier, a good knowledge of the product and its promotion is very important.

2. **Name of interviewee:** Jerry Plante

Interviewee's profession: Former Mann USA

Duration of the interview: 25 minutes

Do you believe the growth of Virncola production has been constant over time?

Many wines have been developed over time, for example, Germany buys wine by season, releases new wines from time to time, and has promotions that help you get to know this market better; but there is still a lot to learn, and it's not well publicized.

Is there an advantage in the wine market?

There are no advantages, as there is not as much marketing to make this product known in its established sector; there are also wines that are not very well known thanks to advertising and communicators.

In terms of substitutes, what are the most competitive products that can replace wine?

Wines compete with spirits, beer, whiskey, etc.

What do you think is the best strategy for entering the market with a new product like orange wine?

A good market strategy is to know the segment you are going to target, taking into account the competition that exists around it, and also to make sure that the public has enough information about the product that will be brought to market, as often sales are made for that very purpose. Promote the product through social media.

How technologically challenging is it to start a wine company?

Starting a business can be a daunting task for many and easy for others, but you need to consider the investment that is required to start a business, especially look for organizations that support entrepreneurial projects and thus have the capital to get started.

Would you recommend orange wine production?

Yes, because there is a market that uses this raw material to produce wine. So with a good market research, knowing the chemical composition and all the necessary studies, it will be possible to establish production.

Is there any state support for the development of domestic winemaking?

The government has created organizations that provide financing for entrepreneurship, so with the help of changing the production matrix, the country wants to grow in terms of quality and use national raw materials to be able to export.

What would you recommend for the production and commercialization of orange wine in the Ecuadorian market?

Make the product known in all aspects and help spread the word about its consumption.

1.1.8 Conclusions

According to the results of the conducted marketing research, it can be concluded that the population consumes wine at least once a month and at the time of purchasing the product does so in various supermarket chains. Most of all the customer's attention is attracted by the taste of wine, its consistency and quality, despite the fact that the surveyed people consumed wines of Chilean and Argentinean origin, among others, they are willing to pay from 10 to 15 dollars for quality wine.

The people surveyed mostly tend to consume wine on special occasions. It was also determined that the presentation and packaging of the product will be made of glass and its volume will be 750 ml, as in the current market.

Having analyzed the results of the study, we will proceed to calculate the expected demand for the consumption of Caluma wine in the city of Guayaquil. It should be noted that, based on this study, we will also define marketing strategies to promote the product.

1.1.9   Expected demand for the product

To determine the demand for Caluma wine in the city of Guayaquil, the following factors were taken into account:

f People between the ages of 20 and 60, which is 1'192.201 residents.

f The percentage of people who drink wine in the city of Guayaquil is 20%, reflecting 238,440 people.

The f % of product acceptance, which is 23%, reflects 54,841 people.

f The average number of people making up a family in the city of Guayaquil is 5.

J According to the survey, a person buys wine at least once a month.

As a result of the above, the following emerges:

J 54,841 / 5 = 10,968 bottles of 750 ml wine per month, which is 131,616 bottles of wine per year.

Considering the fact that we cannot count on this demand as it is excessive, it was decided to produce 60% units per year, which will bring the total to 78,960 units.

3.3   SWOT ANALYSIS

Strengths

- CALUMA wine has rich characteristics as it is made from orange.
- VINOS DEL PACIFICO S.A. uses domestic raw materials.
- CALUMA orange wine will be competitively priced compared to other wines.
- The company has trained employees in all areas of the business.

Weaknesses

- Dissemination occurs only at the local level.
- Small variety of products.
- Consumer distrust due to the introduction of a new product to the market.
- Lack of equity capital.
- Lack of strategic outlets for CALUMA wine.
- Lack of technological equipment.

Opportunities

- Government support for small businesses.
- Variety of substitute products.
- Increased sales of Caluma wine; due to the increase in population in the city of Guayaquil.
- Introducing CALUMA wine to a new, fast-growing market segment.
- Opening Franchises.
- Favorable market trend.

Threats

- Political instability.

- Competencies already on the market.
- Restrictions on bank lending.
- Potential competitors in the wine market offering lower prices.
- Potential taxes on the product.
- Response of existing competitors.

3.4 MARKETING PLAN

3.4.1 Marketing mix

3.4.1.1 Product. VINOS DEL PACIFICO S.A. will produce and sell wine made from orange.

The presentation of the CALUMA wine will be 750 ml, the packaging will be in a glass bottle with cork, it will comply with quality standards that assure the consumer that the product they consume has the appropriate safety and hygiene, as well as the properties that the product has because it is orange.

CALUMA WINE Differentiating Factors.

f A beverage containing nutrients that are beneficial to the health of consumers.

f Made from orange, which contains many nutrients.

f 100% natural beverage.

f Contributing to the preservation of the environment with glass packaging.

Why use glass containers?

From an environmental point of view, glass packaging has the following advantages:

Production:

f The cost of production is low because the raw materials for its production are very expensive.

f They are often made of material that is inactive and therefore does not pollute the environment.

f Glass objects are reusable.

f The glass formulation may vary depending on the type of packaging required or the specific application.

f Will not rust or lose its attractiveness during use, except when used outdoors.

J It is a clean, immaculate, hygienic material, suitable and waterproof for everyday use.

J They must not be drilled with sharp agents.

Slogan:

"Quality, consistency and change.

This slogan was chosen because it mentions three words that will be emphasized about the product. The word "quality" - because the product will be developed through a comprehensive process that reflects its harmlessness. The word "permanence" - because it stands out from the original material for its benefits and the fact that it does not disappear so easily. And finally, the word "change" - because it is a wine from a country with a different flavor from its competitors.

Logo: The logo is designed on the principle of origin, which emphasizes the canton of Caluma, province of Bolivar.

Figure 27 Caluma Wine logo
Source: Mana Fernanda Ladines and Diana Pineda, 2018

Description of services

The service provided is aimed at guiding the customer during the purchase of the product, so that the consumer feels at ease when buying, is aware of the product and the price, so that he can purchase a quality product according to his budget.

For this, the company will have trained staff in all areas, meaning all employees will have the same productivity.

Strategy: To bring to the national market a wine whose raw material (orange) comes from Petis, thereby enhancing all its properties and nutrients, identifying positive aspects for the health of consumers and ensuring the positioning of the product.

Purpose: To meet customer needs and preferences by providing a quality product that stands out from the competition.

Tactics:

ƒ Conduct tastings at outlets established under the project before its market launch to see if it meets the expectations of potential customers and/or to correct the c;ii';icleiislic;is of the project.

ƒ Use a label that communicates the composition of the product and, above all, emphasizes its benefits.

Product Characteristics: the CALUMA wine will have the identifying and differentiating characteristics detailed below:

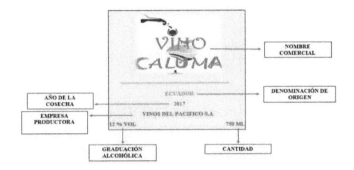

Figure 29 Rear product label
Source: *Maria Fernanda Ladines and Diana Pineda, 2018*

Figure 28 Product front label
Source: *Maria Fernanda Ladines and Diana Pineda, 2018*

3.4.1.2 Price. Setting a price is very important because it is a way to convince our consumers to buy the product.

The following aspects were taken into account when setting the price:

S Production costs

S Competitors' prices

J Price depending on the economic situation of the consumer.

J Price that customers are willing to pay

The price of this product will be $10.00.

Goal: To establish CALUMA wine as a competitive product by pricing it without sacrificing its quality.

Tactic: Set a $10.00 price on the product so that it is accepted by consumers and represents the quality of the product as such.

3.4.1.3 Location. The place of sale of CALUMA WINE will be the city of Guayaquil, as the market research was conducted in this city, but in the future the distribution could be extended to different regions of the country.

When we talk about variable area or distribution, we have to take into account aspects related to:

Distribution channels: Caluma wines will be distributed directly to supermarkets, minimarkets and liquor stores in the city of Guayaquil.

3.4.1.4   Promotion. It consists of the use of mass media. This strategy is usually used to reach the target audience quickly and intensively, for medium or short-term effects with benefits directly translating into sales. The media include:

Television J

J Press (specialized magazines, newspapers)

J Printed materials (brochures, banners, etc.)

J Social media

J Promotional bells at points of sale (supermarkets)

J Word-of-mouth promotion (product recommendation)

3.4.1.5   Customer Loyalty. To retain our customers or keep them loyal, during the peak season, that is, from July to December, we run promotions where for every wine they bring in, they will receive a discount on another purchase. If you bring two wines, the first one will be charged as normal and the second one will be half-price, provided the wine you choose has a red label with the word "promo" on it.

In this way, our customers will feel satisfied by taking not only one wine, but more. In addition, every time they will make a purchase, they will have to give a small evaluation of the service offered, where it will be categorized as: satisfactory, good, ordinary or bad. In this way, the company will know how its customers feel about the service and will be able to improve it.

3.5 MARKET SEGMENTATION

Global market

There are several companies in the world that produce and sell wine, so its demand among the major wine producing countries in Europe, especially in North America and Asia, is beginning to expand, causing the development of international wine trade (Piazza, 2017).

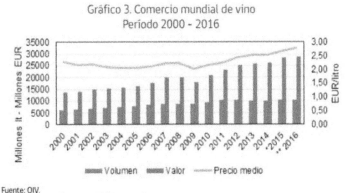

Fuente: OIV.
* 2015: cifras provisionales; 2016: cifras predictivas

Figure 30 World wine production data
Source: International Wine Organization

Geographical segmentation

Men and women of socio-economic level "C" of the typical middle class located in the north of the city of Guayaquil.

Demographic segmentation

The aim is to identify variables such as age, occupation, income, family size, nationality of potential consumers and others.

With this segmentation, we identify a possible consumer profile for the company that has certain characteristics: men and women who have a stable job, formal or informal, a minimum income of 800 dollars, Ecuadorian or foreign citizenship.

All these variables not only segment the market but also help to form an econometric model for VINOS DEL PACIFICO S.A..

Psychographic segmentation

It seeks to identify people with normal lifestyles and developed buying habits who seek to fulfill their needs when consuming beverages, where the buyer focuses not only on the product but also on the benefits it brings to the consumer - this is the need that "VINOS DEL PACIFICO SA" seeks to fulfill.

Segmentation of customer loyalty or behavior

Customers can be segmented based on customer loyalty. They may remain loyal to certain brands, stores or companies. This is based on the benefits a product provides at the time of purchase and whether it meets the customer's expectations and needs.

The product offered by VINOS DEL PACIFICO SA must meet the requirements of a changing market and fully take into account the needs of the customer, so that the product satisfies not only social needs but also the self-esteem of the customer, and thus positioned as the first choice when buying wine.

3.5.1 Target markets

The study population was located in: Urdesa, Saukes, Samanes and Ciudadela Universitaria.

Characterization of the target population:

Age:	20 to 60 years old
Employment:	Formal or informal
Household income:	According to the average of the data
(INEC, Ecuador en	
	figures) in the amount of $841.

Socio-economic level "C" (middle class) According to (Ecuador en cifras, 2011)

Table 21 Population Characteristics
Source: Mana Fernanda Ladines and Diana Pineda, 2018

3.5.2 Positioning

Market positioning is determining the place of your product or service in relation to other companies offering similar products or services in the marketplace and in the minds of the consumer.

In an oversaturated market with many products or services offering similar benefits, good positioning sets a brand or product apart from the rest, giving it the opportunity to set a higher price and set back competitors on results.

Proper brand positioning, market positioning also allows the product and the company that produces it to overcome bad seasons more easily. It also gives the brand or product more flexibility to expand, change, distribute and advertise.

The following are the basic steps to take:

ƒ Market segmentation

ƒ Evaluation of each segment

ƒ Selecting a segment (or segments) to target

ƒ Identification of different positioning opportunities for each selected segment

ƒ Selection and development of a positioning concept (VELASQUEZ, 2015).

Our product is a project product unlike other existing competitors, but to achieve positioning of both the company and the product, we are going to conduct product tastings so that people can have confidence in the product, we are also going to set up points of sale where we will provide extensive information about the product and in this way the consumer will know the benefits of the product.

3.6 TECHNICAL ANALYSIS

3.6.1 Product Analysis

Chemical and physical components:

- Water: its share is between 82 and 88 %.
- Alcohol: formed by fermentation and gives body and flavor to the wine. It ranges from 7 to 17%, depending on the type of wine.
- Sugars: affect the flavor of wine.
- Tannins: Give color and texture to wine.
- Volatile substances: part of the flavor.
- Acids: involved in shaping the flavor of wine.

3.6.2 Block diagram of the Caluma wine production process

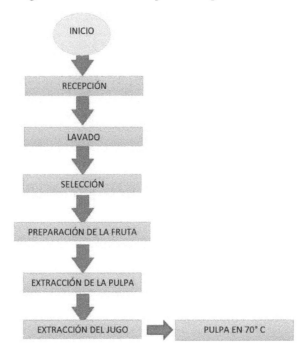

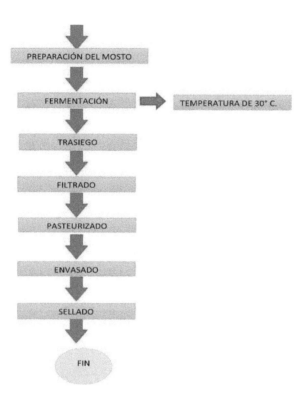

3.6.3 Production tasks

> Produce Caluma wine in the amount of 78,960,750 ml bottles per year.

> Produce quality orange wine that is safe for consumers.

> Efficient utilization of all company resources.

> Industrial production of other fruits such as apples, mangoes, etc.

3.6.4 Product Specifications

Vino Caluma uses good quality oranges as it is an Iraida from the canton of Caluma, a place where oranges grow in abundance, in a superb presentation.

They will be made through an alcoholic fermentation process, so the alcohol content is achieved naturally rather than added as in many other drinks.

Costs

• **Labor**

The cost of labor will be specified by the Department of Labor.

- **Raw materials**

The cost of raw materials, given that the suppliers are located in Bolivar City, Caluma, is given in this market.

- **Electricity, drinking water, telephone**

The cost of these utilities is normal as the project area is considered an urban growth area.

Availability of raw materials

The supply of raw materials and supplies in terms of quantity and quality is one of the most important aspects to be developed by the project.

The location of the project allows access to fruit suppliers at all times as it is located within the country.

3.6.5 Suppliers

The suppliers of direct raw materials are orange growers located in the canton of Caluma. Indirect materials, such as glass containers and corks, will be purchased through the company Envases del Litoral, located in the city of Guayaquil at kilometer 12 of Daule Street, the same company responsible for the distribution of containers to the different sectors. An evaluation of suppliers will also be carried out on a quarterly basis.

Please see the vendor evaluation form in **Attachment 1** below.

3.6.6 Amenities
Geographical location of facilities

VINOS DEL PACIFICO SA will have its premises in the canton of Caluma. It represents 4.5% of the territory of Bolívar Province (about 0.2 thousand km2).
(SI - DIRECTORATE OF METHODS, 2014)

Población:	13.1 mil hab. (7.1% respecto a la provincia de BOLÍVAR).
Urbana:	47.7%
Rural:	52.3%
Mujeres:	50.4%
Hombres:	49.6%
PEA:	47.7% (6.9% de la PEA de la provincia de BOLÍVAR)

Table 22 Population and Housing Census 2010
Source: INEC

An important advantage is that the canton of Calumet is one of the main producers of oranges in the country, the raw material that will be used to produce the company's wine. Services such as water, electricity and telephone are efficiently provided.

Land and buildings

To set up a company, you need to lease a plant of sufficient size to house the winery and equipment.

The company will have dimensions of 50 meters long by 50 meters wide which will include the areas of general management, administration and finance, marketing, sales and marketing, human talent and production/quality, it will also have a laboratory, warehouse and finished product storage. It will have a meeting room next to rest rooms and additionally a 15 square meter processing plant.

Labor

According to the number of wines to be produced each month, 20 operators working 5 days a week for 40 hours a day will be able to fulfill the production tasks set, especially because there are periods of fermentation and aging in wine production when the control and activities to be carried out are not labor intensive and the intervention of the operators is brief. On the administrative side, in the area of human talent, the recruitment of personnel and the payment of the corresponding salaries will be carried out.

Infrastructure and environment

The site has all the basic services needed for this project.

The site is free of pollution, which is very important for wine production processes, so the location of the company will not affect the person or their surroundings.

Climate

The sector where the company is located has an ideal climate for the realization of the project, with an average temperature of 22°C, which is optimal for this type of project.

Quality control of processes

Quality control is very important in wine production, because it determines whether the product will be accepted by the target market. In order to obtain a good wine and guarantee the proper quality of the beverage, it is necessary to follow the necessary rules during the fermentation and processing of the product to avoid the appearance of undesirable microorganisms.

During fermentation, it is very important to monitor the fermentation process by measuring Brix and pH.

In order to achieve the above objectives, staff participation is very important in the production process as it enables the successful execution of all hygiene related operations.

3.6.7 Equipment and machinery

According to the production operations that the company must perform to obtain its products, it is necessary to have the necessary equipment and inventory. It is important to note that the capacities installed allow for the production of products that satisfy the demand determined during the market research.

The implements to be used are as follows:

> **Selection table**

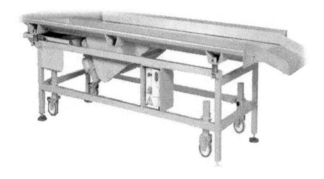

Figura 31   Selection Table
Source : http://www.imvaieretti.com.ar/vinificacion.html

> **Sinking tub**

Figura 32   Wash tub
Source : http://www.equiposantequera.com/categoria-producto/inoxidables/fregaderos/

> **Metal stripping machine**

Figura 33   Metal stripping machine
Source : http://www.equiposantequera.com/categoria-producto/inoxidables/fregaderos/

> Electronic scales, load capacity 500 kg

Figura 34   Electronic scales
Source : http://balanzasperu.com/balanza-de-plataforma-en-lima.html

> Hydraulic breaker, stainless steel, capacity 500 kg

Figura 35   Pulper
Source : http://www.portaldelcampo.cl/verAnuncio/2274/despulpadora.html

> Air conditioning tank, capacity 300 kg

Figura 36   Air conditioning tank
Source : http://www.giurgola.com/product-showcase/acqua/

> Fermentation tank, capacity 200 kg

Figura 37   Fermentation vessel
Source : http://urbinavinos.blogspot.com/2012/03/depositos-de-fermentacion-y.html

> Filling machine, 200 kg capacity

Figura 38   rigging machine
Source : https://www.agrieuro.es/bombas-de-trasiego-c-107.html

> Plate filter, capacity 200 kg

Figura 39   Plate filters
Source : http://www.directindustry.es/prod/mori-tem/product-99195-1617555.html

> **Packaging machine, 500 kg capacity**

Figura 40   Packing machine
Source : *https://equitek.com.mx/*

> **Spectrophotometer**

Figura 41   Spectrophotometer
Source : *https://elespectrofotometro.com/espectrofotometria-uv-visible/*

The technology used to produce Caluma wine is specialized for this type of product, so the equipment can be used in other production lines. This feature of the technology is an important advantage, since the company can diversify its production, and in case of unsatisfactory results or anticipation of a crisis, the technology will not be an obstacle to cease operations.

There are many options available for purchasing office equipment, furniture and supplies:

This document does not indicate who the final supplier will be, however they have been listed in various retail outlets in the city and online. The value of these investments or company assets is detailed in the financial valuation of the business.

Form of equipment purchase

Acquisition of equipment at the plant will be by direct purchase and training in its use will be the responsibility of the equipment suppliers who will provide the necessary instructions for its use.

Production personnel

The operational staff for the plant operation is distributed as follows:

REQUIRED POSITION	NUMBER OF PEOPLE
Reception operators	
Pulp production operators	
Fermentation Manager	
Filter operators	
Packaging and sealing operators	
Bodeguero	1
ALL	

Table 23 Production personnel
Source: Mana Fernanda Ladines and Diana Pineda, 2018

Maintenance and spare parts policy

The maintenance, repair and modernization activities for equipment and machinery are described in the maintenance policy, which aims to ensure the continuous operation of the equipment, and defines the needs for personnel, materials, financial resources and organizational structure to achieve the objectives set by VINOS DEL PACIFICO SA.

Company personnel should make constant checks on equipment using checklists that detail each piece of equipment and the function it performs. In this way, it will be known whether the equipment is working properly or is lacking maintenance; to do this, personnel must be trained and qualified to do the job.

Forms of work

The plant will operate on only one 8-hour shift, and responsible personnel will leave the plant clean and tidy, with no residue from the previous process.

3.6.8 Plant distribution

To ensure the availability of the required raw materials, the location was chosen because of the proximity of suppliers, which facilitates and speeds up transportation and immediate delivery to meet production requirements, and is located in an industrial sector, which meets the company's expectations for its installation.

We lease a 50 m² factory with a 50 m² warehouse suitable for the production of food products such as wine, where raw materials will be received and processed, within the same warehouse will be administrative offices, but at the same time separated from the production area, between them general manager, operations manager, marketing and sales manager under appropriate economic and security conditions for ease of communication and control in the production of wine.

The factory has 1 parking lot and 4 bathrooms and locker rooms for employees.

Company map "VINOS DEL PAOTICO SA" 50 m

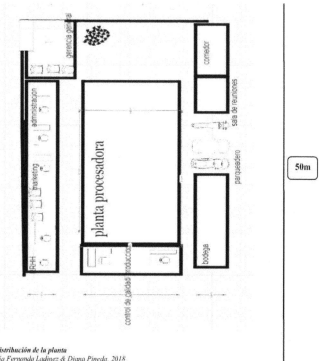

Figura 42 Distribución de la planta
Fuente: María Fernanda Ladinez & Diana Pineda, 2018

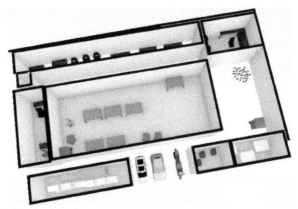

Figure 43 3D schematic of the plant
Source: Mana Fernanda Ladines and Diana Pineda, 2018

3.6.9 Control systems
Critical quality processes

Critical quality points for Caluma winemaking are must preparation, as various substances are added to the must, which are then measured. Also fermentation, which requires precise temperatures, and then racking to remove particles.

Quality control points

Quality assurance items include:

- Receiving raw materials
- Precise pulp temperature
- Measuring the amount of solutes added to the juice
- Checking the air trap
- Checking the sterilized strainer

- Make sure glass bottles and stoppers are in good condition.
A detailed fact sheet is provided in **Appendix 2.**

3.7 MANAGEMENT ANALYSIS

3.7.1 Business Group
Vinos del Pacifico S.A. consists of an anonymous company, some details of which are described below.

- Vinos del Pacifico SA will consist of 4 partners who make up the highest authority.
- Policies and rules will be developed to govern the company.
- Appoint a general manager.
- They make decisions on matters concerning the company.

3.7.2 Human Resources
The Vinos del Pacifico S.A. organization will employ trained personnel to perform its assigned functions.

3.7.3 Organizational chart

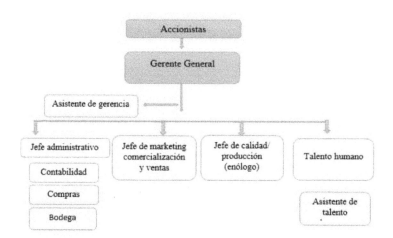

Figure 44 Organizational structure of the company
Source: Mana Fernanda Ladines and Diana Pineda, 2018

3.7.4 Staff job profiles

POSITION	FUNCTION	PROFILE
GENERAL MANAGER	> Allocate all leadership positions. > Conduct periodic evaluation of the performance of the functions of the various departments. > Plan and develop short- and long-term goals and objectives and hold the annual	Education: Master's degree in Management or International Business, Bachelor's degree in Business Administration, Bachelor's degree in Economics, Bachelor's degree in International Business Administration Finance. Skills: Good verbal skills, good attitude and ability, disposition and know-how.

	forecasts of these goals for approval by the company's management. > Coordinate with administrative offices to ensure that records and their analysis are done correctly.	Education: Knowledge of business processes and business environment. elaborationde beverages. Experience: at least 3 years in the field.
TALENT MANAGEMENT DIRECTOR HUMAN TALENT ASSISTANT HUMAN	Coordinate all functions performed in the department > Coordinate all functions performed in the department > Company Recruitment and Training Delegate	Education: Degree Bachelor's degree site organizational psychology Administrationde Human Resources. Skills: Leadership, results-oriented, committed to the company and employees, objective and organized. Formation: Define and manage staffing levels.
		ManagementSite existing staff. Experience: at least 3 years in this position.
ADMINISTRATIVE HEAD COUNTER	The administration is responsible for purchasing and accounting department Administrator for analysis, economic resource management and responsible for control of financial information.	Education: commercial engineering, administration, Econoniti or related majors Skills: Proactivity, disposition, risk management, communication and leadership skills. Education: Extensive knowledge of financial accounting, knowledge of local and global financial regulations. Work experience: at least 3 years.

MARKETING MANAGER MARKETING AND. SALES.	Analyze and track sales and compare it to competitors. Design policy for advertising, promotion, distribution and presentation of the product. Control of the return of finished goods delivered to the concession. Constantly look for potential clients to have a steady income.	Education: marketing engineer, Marketing or related professions. Skills: clear customer focus and ability to strategize. Formation: Knowledge planning commercial strategies, sales channels, Competition research, customer orientation Creative thinking Experience: 3 years.
CUSTOMER SERVICE	> Take measurements to find out customer satisfaction. > Preventing the causes of conflicts with customers.	Education: License. Completed - Intern. Skills: Friendliness and useful with suppliers and customers,
	Receive and resolve complaints and grievances. Analyze possible processes that affect the organization's customers. Propose solutions for these processes. Generate and display results on measurements customer satisfaction. Explore the reasons for customer dissatisfaction.	tolerable. Education: English advanced. Experience: 2-3 years in a customer service environment.
MANUFACTURER QUALITY/PRODUCTION	> Responsible for the entire wine production process including raw material reception, storage, analysis, preservation, bottling and wine quality. > Time control in	Education: License. Oenology, engineer Quinico, Agro-Industrial, Foodor Quality Systems Engineers. Skills: Good attitude, leadership,

	production process. Provide care for equipment, machinery and tools. product rotation during the process (fermentation and maturation) and finished product.	teamwork, Formation: know the winemaking process, the skill of the staff. Experience: 3 years in this position.
PLANT DIRECTOR	> He is responsible for the application of wine inspection measures at the winery, supervising the maintenance staff.	Education: Chemical, food, agro-industrial or quality systems engineer. Formation: familiarization with the process of wine production. Skills: team player, good with words. Work experience: mmimo 2 years
OPERATORS	> Those who are responsible for the product development process.	Education: Education mmima Bachelor's Degree. Formation: knowledge in
		production area drinks or food . Work Experience: 6 months

3.8 AUXILIARY ORGANIZATIONS

- **Emprendecuador under the Ministry of Coordination of Production, Employment and Competitiveness.**

The EmprendEcuador program, promoted by the Ministry of Coordination of Production, Employment and Competitiveness (MCPEC), encourages citizens passionate about creating enterprises with growth potential, transformative or highly differentiated, with great potential to enter the international arena.

- **CreEcuador**

The CreEcuador program aims to stimulate productive and territorial development in the Pinas by providing access to business ownership. It does this by using programs and tools to help implement productive transformation projects that contribute to progress in different regions of the country.

- **IIEPRO**

The Ministry of Industry and Productivity, through the FONDEPYME program, aims to help improve the conditions and capacities of small and medium-sized enterprises, individual or group, that produce quality goods or services at the national level.

- **Ministry of Economic and Social Inclusion**

Through the National Institute of Popular and Solidarity Economy, MIES aims to stimulate the popular and solidarity economy through impulse, promotion and forecasting of the production, distribution and consumption of goods and services to contribute to the realization of the good life.

- **National Finance Corporation**

National Finance Corporation offers a wide range of loans that can help entrepreneurs.

IFC Regulations

GENERAL CONDITIONS	
ULTIMATE BENEFICIARY	Natural or legal persons Creditworthy trusts may be considered trusts that have already been established, have applied for a line of credit, and have the contractual, financial and legal conditions to be creditworthy, in which case their founders are co-borrowers.
FUNDING PERCENTAGE	Financing of complex housing construction projects of the horn stage, up to 80% of the investment plan, depending on internal analysis. Land must be provided by the client.
DEADLINE	Up to 5 years
PERIOD OF GRACE	Up to 24 months depending on the project and its cash flow

PURCHASE PORTFOLIO AND WORKING CAPITAL FINANCING CONSTRUCTION FOR SALE	
VOYAGE	Financing obligations through the public and private financial system, preserving the ultimate goal of the transaction: working capital construction for sale.
FUNDING PERCENTAGE	The acquired operation can be refinanced and a new expansion loan can be provided as part of CFN Construye's financing.

ACQUISITION OF A PORTFOLIO OF LOANS FOR HOUSING PROJECTS	

GENERAL CONDITIONS	• Acquisition of portfolio of loans issued by financial institutions for housing projects (VIP) • Projects in progress, i.e. not yet fully completed. • The total amount of credits will be up to 80% of the total investment plan of the project based on internal analysis. • Projects must meet the conditions defined in the CFN Construye - Priority Housing Construction (VIP) line.
BENEFICIARY OF THE PORTFOLIO PURCHASE	Public or private financial institutions legally established in Ecuador (including liquidated IFIS).
DEBTOR	Natural or legal person
PORTFOLIO PURCHASE TERMS	• Portfolio rating: based on the analysis of the project. • Method of acquisition: maximum at par as negotiated. • Term: up to 1800 days - 5 years. • Portfolio type: commercial, with a balance greater than $50,000. • Maximum amount: $25,000,000 per borrower and $50,000,000 per economic group. • The acquired portion of the portfolio is transferred at the current interest rate at which it was provided to the MFI that transferred the portfolio: at the new financing that will be provided at the current CFN Construye rate.
ADDITIONAL FUNDING	• Payment of obligations purchased from national suppliers. • Working capital: Continue to expand the real estate project. in accordance with the terms of CFN regulations. The funding should cover the full completion of the project about the respective phase.
These loans may be refinanced, additional financing may be provided to borrowers or debtors.	

3.9 LEGAL ANALYSIS

3.9.1 Legal aspects

- The constitution of the company under the authority of Konipani

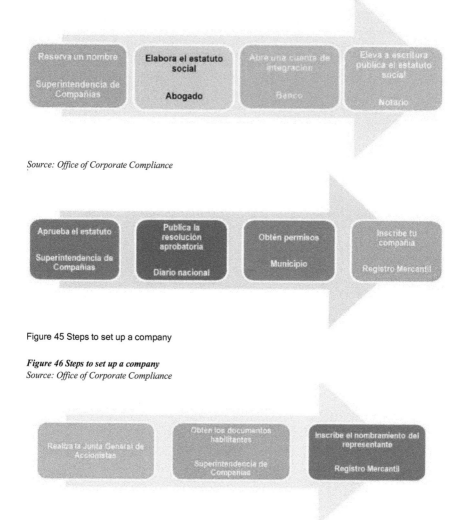

Source: Office of Corporate Compliance

Figure 45 Steps to set up a company

Figure 46 Steps to set up a company
Source: Office of Corporate Compliance

Figure 47 Stages of business registration
Source: Commercial Register

3.9.2 Requirements for obtaining an RUC

- The form must be filled out completely

- Original and copy of the memorandum of **association**

- Original and copies of appointments

- Copies of partners' identification cards and voting certificates

3.10 ENVIRONMENTAL ANALYSIS

Environmental management system

Organizations of all kinds are increasingly concerned about taking and marking the right environmental stance, testing the environmental impact of their actions and products, and achieving environmental goals.

These decisions may be driven by customer requirements, the market, government regulations, etc. Increasingly, however, organizations are looking for new ways to add value to their products and services, so establishing an environmental management system (EMS) is a great help in organizing a company's goals.

ISO 14000 standard

This standard specifies requirements for an environmental management system that enables an organization to express its policies and objectives, taking into account legal requirements and information on significant environmental impacts.

ISO 14001 applies to those environmental aspects that an organization can manage and over which it should have control, although it does not itself set specific environmental performance criteria.

This standard applies to any organization that wishes to do so:

- Implement, maintain and improve the environmental management system;
- Ensure compliance with established environmental policies;
- Demonstrate this compliance to third parties;
- Apply for certification/registration of your environmental management system by an external organization;
- Conduct self-assessment and self-declaration in accordance with this standard.

All requirements of this standard are intended to be incorporated into any environmental management system, the applicability of which will depend on factors such as the environmental policy of the organization, the nature of its activities and the environment in which it operates.

Risk matrix

A risk matrix is a powerful tool to balance the most significant risks inherent in a company's operations, whether it be processes, products or services.

Characteristics of the risk matrix

To ensure that the risk matrix is effective and useful, it should have the following characteristics:

f It must be flexible.

f Ease of production and consultation.

f For objective diagnosis of a set of risk factors.

f Be able to compare projects, areas and activities.

The risk matrix is detailed below, see appendix 2.

3.11 SOCIAL ANALYSIS

VINOS DEL PACIFICO SA is a company with growth impact at national and international level, which since its opening has provided jobs for many people in Ecuador, teaming up with several national suppliers to promote employment and the production of raw materials. The raw material is orange, which has beneficial properties that reduce the risk of disease.

3.11.1 Possibility of rejection or support from the community

Caluma orange wine is likely to be accepted because it fits into the drinks required for a meeting. The product has a low alcohol content, so it is not harmful when consumed in moderation, it does not contain harmful substances to the body, and the container can be recycled.

The drink acts as an alternative to traditional side dishes during dinners and meals in general. It helps people find a greater variety of foods to consume.

The company complies with quality, safety and environmental standards compliant with ISO 9001, ISO 14001 and OHSAS 8001, as well as with the country's legislation, which guarantees minimal impact on the environment and the society in which it operates.

The company implements consistent internal codes of conduct that promote environmental stewardship, hiring people from the communities where the company is located, and policies that promote work-life balance among employees.

3.11.2 Additional services that the company requires from the community

VINOS DEL PACIFICO, as a business plan, has a community cultural development plan and a social responsibility program for moderate consumption of alcoholic beverages.

The company strives to increase social and gender diversity in the organization and will be sought after by the existing surrounding community. The social image of the company is shaped by the adopted company policy, its commitment to corporate social responsibility and care for the environment.

The company's Code of Ethics is aimed at educating employees on values and principles consistent with corporate social responsibility, which contributes to strengthening the company's image.

The Company adheres to a basic principle: a company as an institution can be considered ethical only when it finds agreement or consensus among all groups affected by its effects.

From this social balance perspective, the company seeks to achieve positive value through ethical balance. To this end, it strives to:

- Identify the stakeholders that the company is converging with.

- Specify the various interests that define each of the groups involved.

- Translate these interests into indicators that measure the distance between the social commitments made. To avoid a partial vision, objective or quantitative indicators should be combined with subjective or qualitative ones.

Chapter IV

FINANCIAL RESEARCH

To start VINOS DEL PACIFICO SA, it is important to determine the initial amount of the project in order to establish the sources of financing that will be used to acquire these resources.

4.1 INITIAL INVESTMENT

The initial investment is made through fixed assets and deferred assets to launch the company.

The initial investment required to launch the company is **$41,015.**

INVESTMENTS.
ORIGINALLY "VINOS DEL PACIFICO S.A.".

Description	Cost
Property, plant and equipment	$ 39.015
Deferred assets	$ 2.000
TOTAL	**$ 41.015**

Table 24 Initial investments
Source: Mana Fernanda Ladines and Diana Pineda, 2018

i. Investments in property, plant and equipment

The fixed assets required for this project are detailed in the initial investment. Their total cost is $39,015, which can be divided into large groups. First, $15,195 will be spent on the assets that require the most investment, as these are the machinery and equipment directly used in production. On the other hand, $3,360 will be needed to buy computer equipment, $5,460 to buy furniture and office equipment, and an automobile will also be bought, with a total cost of $39,015.

valued at $15,000, to be considered for offering at city car dealerships.

Property, plant and equipment of vinos del pacifico s.a.	Cost

		$ 15.195
Machinery and equipment		$ 15.195
Computer equipment		$ 3.360
Office furniture and equipment		$ 5.460
Vehicles		$ 15.000
TOTAL PROPERTY, PLANT AND EQUIPMENT		**$ 39.015**

Table 25 Investments in property, plant and equipment
Source: Mana Fernanda Ladines and Diana Pineda, 2018

ii. Machinery and equipment

Vinos del Pacifico S.A. Machinery and Equipment.

Machinery and equipment	Quantity	Unit cost	Total cost
Selection table (stainless steel) with a size of 2x2 meters		$ 235	$ 705
Wash tub (stainless steel) 3 meters	1	$ 450	$ 450
Metal stripping machine (stainless steel)	1	$ 1.300	$ 1.300
Electronic scales, load capacity 500 kg		$ 120	$ 240
Pulper (stainless steel)	1	$ 1.300	$ 1.300
Conditioning tank capacity (stainless steel) 300 kg		$ 900	$ 1.800
Fermentation tank (stainless steel) with a capacity of 200 kg		$ 500	$ 2.000
Rack (stainless steel) with a load capacity of 200 kg		$ 500	$ 1.000
Plate filter (stainless steel) with a capacity of 200 kg	1	$ 900	$ 900
Packing machine (stainless steel) with a capacity of 500 kg	1	$ 2.000	$ 2.000
Indurama brand refrigerator		$ 500	$ 1.000
Spectrophotometer (for measuring alcohol)		$ 500	$ 1.000
Laboratory equipment	10	$ 50	$ 500
Others	?	$ 1.000	$ 1.000
Total		$ 8.705	$ 15.195

Table 26 Investments in machinery and equipment
Source: Maria Fernanda Ladines and Diana Pineda, 2018

iii. Computer equipment

VINOS DEL PACIFICO S.A. COMPUTER EQUIPMENT.			
Computer equipment	**Quantity**	**C.U.**	**C.T.**
DELL desktop computer		$ 400	$ 2.400

Wireless routers		$ 60	$ 360
EDSON multifunctional printer.		$ 300	$ 600
ALL		**$ 760**	**$ 3.360**

Table 27 Investments in computer equipment
Source: Mana Fernanda Ladines and Diana Pineda, 2018

iv. **Office furniture and equipment**

VINOS DEL PACIFICO S.A. OFFICE FURNITURE AND EQUIPMENT.			
Furniture and equipment	**Quantity**	**C.U.**	**C.T.**
Executive desks		$ 100	$ 700
Swivel executive chairs		$ 50	$ 200
Chairs		$ 30	$ 90
Waiting chairs with armrests		$ 30	$ 90
Computers		$ 400	$ 2.400
Wireless routers		$ 60	$ 360
Multifunction printers		$ 300	$ 600
Cordless phones		$ 20	$ 80
Office supplies (calculators, staplers, etc.)	10	$ 20	$ 200
Filing cabinets		$ 50	$ 100
garbage cans		$ 10	$ 40
Air conditioner		$ 300	$ 600
ALL		**$ 1.290**	**$ 5.460**

Table 28 Investments in office furniture and equipment
Source: Mana Fernanda Ladines and Diana Pineda, 2018

4.2 VARIABLE COSTS

These are costs that depend on the level of production.

4.2.1 Raw material budget Direct

Direct raw materials are all the basic materials and inputs that make up the product.

To produce **6,580** 750 ml bottles of wine per month, 8,000 kg of oranges and the corresponding amount of sugar and wine yeast are needed, which implies a monthly cost of $2,750.

Monthly and annual raw material budgets and corresponding 5-year forecasts are summarized below.

VINOS DEL PACIFICO S.A. COMMODITY BUDGET.					
Formula for the production of 6580 750 ml bottles					
Description	Unit	Quantity	Unit cost	Total monthly cost	Annual cost
Orange	kg	8.000	$ 0,25	$ 2.000	$ 24.000
Sugar	kg	500	$ 0,70	$ 350	$ 4.200
Wine yeast	Gr	4.000	$ 0,10	$ 400	$ 4.800
ALL			$1,30	$ 2.750	$ 33.000

Table 29 Raw material budget
Source: Mana Fernanda Ladines and Diana Pineda, 2018

Increase in the cost of raw materials in the next 5 years

The percentage of the inflation rate corresponding to 2017, which is 1.1%, which is the increase in goods and services during this period, will be chosen to increase the cost of raw materials over the next 5 years.

ANOS	Raw materials rose 1.1%.
Year 1	$ 33.000
Year 2	$ 33.363
Year 3	$ 33.730
Year 4	$ 34.101
Year 5	$ 34.476

Table 30 Increase in the cost of raw materials
Source: Mana Fernanda Ladines and Diana Pineda, 2018

4.2.2 Budget for direct materials

Direct materials are those items that form an ancillary part in the presentation of the product, in this case bottles, corks and labels, it takes a total of **$32,907.00** monthly to produce **6,580** 750 ml bottles.

The monthly and annual direct materials budget and the corresponding 5-year forecast are presented below.

DIRECT MATERIALS BUDGET VINOS DEL PACIFICO S.A..					
Formula for the production of 6580 750 ml bottles					
Description	block	quantity	unit cost	total monthly expenses	annual cost
750 ml bottle	Unit	6580	$ 2,00	$ 21.938	$ 263.256
Traffic	Unit	6580	$ 0,50	$ 5.484,50	$ 65.814,00
Tags	Unit	6580	$ 0,50	$ 5.485	$ 65.820
ALL			$ 3,00	$ 32.907,00	$ 394.890,00

Table 31 Direct materials budget
Source: Mana Fernanda Ladines and Diana Pineda, 2018

ANOS	Increase in direct materials 1.1%
Year 1	**$ 394.890**
Year 2	$ 399.234
Year 3	$ 403.625
Year 4	$ 408.065
Year 5	$ 412.554

Table 32 Increase in direct materials
Source: Mana Fernanda Ladines and Diana Pineda, 2018

4.2.3 Budget for direct labor costs

It is what is needed to turn raw materials into a finished product. The company will have a total of 20 employees who will be paid a base salary of $386 plus statutory benefits, giving a monthly cost of $9,032 and an annual cost of $108,378.

DIRECT SALARY BUDGET				"VINOS DEL PACIFICO S.A."			
				ADVANTAGES LAW			
	N° OF	WAGE.	Tenth	Tenth	Total	Total	

POSITION	PERSONS	MONTHLY	third	room	monthly	annually
Reception operators		$ 1.158	$ 97	$ 97	$ 1.352	$ 16.218
Operators Despulpanan		$ 1.544	$ 128	$ 128	$ 1.800	$ 21.600
Responsible for fermentation		$ 1.554	$ 128	$ 128	$ 1.810	$ 21.720
Filter operators		$ 1.554	$ 128	$ 128	$ 1.810	$ 21.720
Packaging operators		$ 1.554	$ 128	$ 128	$ 1.810	$ 21.720
Sealing	1	$ 386	$ 32	$ 32	$ 450	$ 5.400
ALL		$ 7.750	$ 641	$ 641	$ 9.032	$ 108.378

Table 33 Salary budget, direct labor
Source: Mana Fernanda Ladines and Diana Pineda, 2018

ANOS	LEVEL MANUAL SALARIES Direct labor $ 11 Annually
Year 1	$ 108.378
Year 2	$ 110.778
Year 3	$ 113.178
Year 4	$ 115.578
Year 5	$ 117.978

Table 34 Wage growth, direct labor
Source: Mana Fernanda Ladines and Diana Pineda, 2018

4.2.4 Supply budget

Budget supplies Vinos del pacifico SA		
Basic services (electricity, water, gas, power, water supply, etc.) drink).	monthly	Annually
		4800

Gloves, glove boxes, buckets, etc.		200	2400
TOTAL		600	7200

Table 35 Supply budget
Source: Mana Fernanda Ladines and Diana Pineda, 2018

ANOS	A 1.1% increase in supply.
Year 1	$ 7.200
Year 2	$ 7.279
Year 3	$ 7.359
Year 4	$ 7.439
Year 5	$ 7.520,00

Table 36 Supply budget
Source: Mana Fernanda Ladines and Diana Pineda, 2018

4.3 FIXED COSTS

These are costs that are independent of the level of production.

4.3.1 Budget for core services and inputs

VINOS DEL PACIFICO SA'S BASIC SERVICES AND SUPPLIES BUDGET.		
Description	**Monthly**	**Annually**
internet services	$ 100	$ 1.200
telephone services	$ 70	$ 840
Cleaning agents	$ 30	$ 360
office supplies	$ 20	$ 240
TOTAL	**$ 220**	**$ 2.640**

Table 37 Budget for core services and inputs
Source: Mana Fernanda Ladines and Diana Pineda, 2018

ANOS	A 1.1% increase in basic services and inputs.

Year 1	$ 2.640
Year 2	$ 2.669
Year 3	$ 2.698
Year 4	$ 2.728
Year 5	$ 2.758

Table 38 Budget for core services and inputs
Source: Mana Fernanda Ladines and Diana Pineda, 2018

4.3.2 Indirect labor

Indirect labor budget of vinos del pacifico s.a..

Position	N° of People	Salary Monthly	Legal benefits		Monthly amount	Annual total
			Thirteenth	Fourteenth		
Quality/Production Manager Plant Manager	$ 1 $ 1	$ 1.000 $ 800	$ 83 $ 67	$ 83 $ 67	$ 1.166 $ 934	$ 13.992 $ 11.208
Total		$ 1.800	$ 150	$ 150	$ 2.100	$ 25.200

Table 39 Budget of direct labor costs
Source: Mana Fernanda Ladines and Diana Pineda, 2018

ANOS	EARNING EARNING WAGE INSTANT WAGE $ 100 per year
Year 1	$ 25.200
Year 2	$ 25.400
Year 3	$ 25.600
Year 4	$ 25.800
Year 5	$ 26.000

Table 40 Increase in direct labor
Source: Mana Fernanda Ladines and Diana Pineda, 2018

4.3.3 Depreciation and amortization of property, plant and equipment

AMORTIZATION OF PROPERTY, PLANT AND EQUIPMENT OF VINOS DEL PACIFICO S.A..								
FIXED ASSETS	COST	ANOS	Ano 2019	Year 2020	Year 2021	Year 2022	Year 2023	ALL
Machinery and equipment Computer equipment Furniture and office equipment	$ 15.195	10	$ 1.270	$ 1.270	$ 1.270	$ 1.270	$ 1.270	$ 6.350
	$ 3.360	5	$ 168	$ 168	$ 168	$ 168	$ 168	$ 840
	$ 5.460	10	$ 129	$ 129	$ 129	$ 129	$ 129	$ 645
Vchiculos	$ 15.000	5	$ 750	$ 750	$ 750	$ 750	$ 750	$ 3.750
Total depreciation and amortization			$ 2.317	$ 2.317	$ 2.317	$ 2.317	$ 2.317	$ 11.585

Table 41 Depreciation of property, plant and equipment
Source: Mana Fernanda Ladines and Diana Pineda, 2018

4.3.4 Deferred assets

This section outlines all the costs that the company must cover before it can start its operations. These costs consist of obtaining permits to register and operate the company, in which a total of $2,000 will be invested.

Amortization of deferred assets

Data

Total deferred assets = $2000

Service life = 5 years

Calculation

Amortization = Deferred Assets / Years of useful life of the project

Amortization = $2000 / 5 years

Amortization = $400

4.4 ADMINISTRATIVE COSTS

4.4.1 Budget for administrative costs

VINOS DEL PACIFICO S.A. ADMINISTRATIVE EXPENSES BUDGET.					
POSITION	WAGE.	ADVANTAGES LAW		TOTAL IN MONTH	TOTAL YEAR
		TEN THIRD	FOUR		

Director General	$ 0,00	$ 0,00	$ 0,00	$ 0,00	$ 0,00
	$ 0,00	$ 0,00	$ 0,00	$ 0,00	$ 0,00
Administrative Manager	$ 900	$ 75	$ 75	$ 1.050	$ 12.600
Assistant to the Head Human	$ 1.000	$ 83	$ 83	$ 1.166	$ 13.996
Resources Manager	$ 400	$ 33	$ 33	$ 466	$ 5.596
Talent Assistant	$ 1.000	$ 83	$ 83	$ 1.166	$ 13.992
Counter	$ 1.000	$ 83	$ 83	$ 1.166	$ 13.992
Head of Marketing and Sales Department	$ 4.300,00	$ 357,67	$ 357,00	$ 5.014,67	$ 60.176,00
ALL					

ANOS	ADMINISTRATIVE COSTS INCREASE $ 100 per year
Year 1	$ 60.176
Year 2	$ 60.876
Year 3	$ 61.576
Year 4	$ 62.276
Year 5	$ 62.976

Table 43 Increase in administrative expenses
Source: Mana Fernanda Ladines and Diana Pineda, 2018

4.4.2 Budget for other expenses

OTHER EXPENDITURES OF THE BUDGET OF VINOS DEL PACIFICO S.A.		
Miscellaneous expenses	Monthly	Annually
Rentals	$ 5.000	$ 60.000
Advertisement	$ 500	$ 6.000
Office supplies	$ 300	$ 3.600
Equipment maintenance	$ 400	$ 4.800
Fuel	$ 200	$ 2.400
ALSO.	$ 6.400	$ 76.800

Table 44 Budget for other expenditures
Source: Mana Fernanda Ladines and Diana Pineda, 2018

ANOS	Increase in other expenses
Year	$ 76.800
Year	$ 77.645

Year	$ 78.499
Year	$ 79.362
Year	$ 80.235

Table 45 Increase in other expenses
Source: Mana Fernanda Ladines and Diana Pineda, 2018

4.5 INVESTMENT SUMMARY

VINOS DEL PACIFICO S.A. Investment Summary.		
Description	Partial value	Total cost
Property, plant and equipment		
Machinery and equipment	$ 15.195	
Computer equipment	$ 3.360	
Office furniture and equipment	$ 5.460	
Vehicles	$ 15.000	
TOTAL PROPERTY, PLANT AND EQUIPMENT		$ 39.015
WORKING CAPITAL PER MONTH		
Deferred assets		
The costs of the constitution	$ 2.000	
Total deferred assets		$ 2.000
VARIABLE COSTS		
Raw materials	$ 2.750	
Direct materials	$ 32.907,00	
Direct labor	$ 9.032	
supplies	$ 600	
FIXED COSTS		
Essential services and supplies	$ 220	
Indirect labor	$ 2.100	
Administrative expenses	$ 5.014,67	
Other expenses	$ 6.400	
TOTAL WORKING CAPITAL PER MONTH		$ 59.024
TOTAL INVESTMENT	$ 100.039	$ 100.039

90

4.6 INVESTMENT FINANCING

It is a set of monetary resources or loans intended for the company to carry out its economic activities, with loans of this type being repayable and supplemented by its own resources to finance investments.

The creation of VINOS DEL PACIFICO S.A. will require an investment of $100,038, which will be 50% financed by CFN (Corporacion Financiera Nacional). will require an investment of $100,038, which will be 50% financed by CFN (Corporacion Financiera Nacional).

VINOS DEL PACIFICO S.A. FINANCING.		
TOTAL AMOUNT	COST	PERCENTAGE
EQUITY CAPITAL	$ 50.019	50%
CREDIT	$ 50.019	50%
ALL	$ 100.038	100%

Table 47 Financing of investments
Source: Mana Fernanda Ladines and Diana Pineda, 2018

4.7 LOAN REPAYMENT

50% of the investment will be financed through CFN (National Finance Corporation) over 5 years at an interest rate of 7.79% per annum, the amortization table is shown below.

LOAN REPAYMENT

Amount	$ 50.019
Number of periods	60 months
Annual interest rate	7,79%
monthly rate	0,63%
Monthly fee	$ 1.146,00

LOAN REPAYMENT

Period	Annual fee	Capital payment	Interests	Credit balance
0				$ 50.019
1	$ 12.458,32	$ 8.561,84	$ 3.896,48	$ 41.457,16
	$ 12.458,32	$ 9.228,81	$ 3.229,51	$ 32.228,35
	$ 12.458,32	$ 9.947,73	$ 2.510,59	$ 22.280,62
	$ 12.458,32	$ 10.722,66	$ 1.735,66	$ 11.557,96
5	$ 12.458,32	$ 11.557,96	$ 900,36	$ 0,00

Table 49 Annual amortization on loans
Source: Mana Fernanda Ladines and Diana Pineda, 2018

4.8 PROJECTED OPERATING EXPENSES

Projected costs		"vinos del pacifico sa".			
Description	Annex 1	Annex 2	Annex 3	Annex 4	Ano 5
Variable costs					
Raw materials	$ 33.000	$ 33.363	$ 33.730	$ 34.101	$ 34.476
Direct materials	$ 394.890	$ 399.234	$ 403.625	$ 408.065	$ 412.554
Direct labor	$ 108.378	$ 110.778	$ 113.178	$ 115.578	$ 117.978
Deliveries	$ 7.200	$ 7.279	$ 7.539	$ 7.439	$ 7.520
All of them	$ 543.468	$ 550.654	$ 558.072	$ 565.183	$ 572.528
Fixed costs					
Basic services and supplies	$ 2.640	$ 2.669	$ 2.698	$ 2.728	$ 2.758
Indirect labor	$ 25.200	$ 25.400	$ 25.600	$ 25.800	$ 26.000
Administrative expenses	$ 60.176	$ 60.876	$ 61.576	$ 62.276	$ 62.976
Other expenses	$ 76.800	$ 77.645	$ 78.499	$ 79.362	$ 80.235
Depreciat and amortization	$ 2.317	$ 2.317	$ 2.317	$ 2.317	$ 2.317
deferred assets	$ 400	$ 400	$ 400	$ 400	$ 400
Interest on loans	$ 3.896	$ 3.230	$ 2.511	$ 1.736	$ 900
All of them	$ 171.429	$ 172.537	$ 173.601	$ 174.619	$ 175.586
Total costs	$ 714.897	$ 723.191	$ 731.673	$ 739.802	$ 748.114
Units produced	78960	80208	81475	82762	84069
Unit cost	$ 9	$ 9	$ 9	$ 9	$ 9

4.9 ESTIMATED INCOME

Revenue is derived from all operations or activities carried out by the company. In order to forecast the annual revenue to be generated from the sale of CALUMA WINE, we determined the percentage of acceptance of the product using the results obtained from a study of wine consumption markets, totaling 78,960 bottles to be produced in the first year.

To estimate the 5-year income, we chose the percentage of the population growth rate of the city of Guayaquil for the period 2001 - 2010, which was 1.58%.

4.9.1 Selling Price

The retail price was set based on market analysis and competition, a price of $10.00 was determined.

Where: The unit cost of production is $9.00 per 750 ml bottle.

UTILITY FORMULA

PROFIT = PVP - UNIT COST OF PRODUCTION

PROFIT = 10 - 9.00

PROFIT = $1.00

The public sale price will be maintained over the 5-year forecast period, allowing the company to be competitive, earning a profit margin from the first year.

4.9.2 Revenue budget

OF THE REVENUE SIDE OF THE "WINE OUT OF THE LIMIT" FICO S.A." [FICO S.A.					
Sales budget	Year 1	Year 2	Year 3	Year 4	Year 5
Wine bottle 750 ml	$78.960	$ 80.208	$81475	$82762	$84069
Selling Price	$ 10	$ 10	$ 10	$ 10	$ 10
TOTAL INCOME	$ 789.600	$ 802.080	$ 814.750	$ 827.620	$ 840.690

Table 51 Revenue budget
Source: Mana Fernanda Ladines and Diana Pineda, 2018

4.10 BREAK-EVEN POINT

The break-even point in a business environment is used to determine the profitability of a project when fixed and variable costs are covered, that is, the company neither gains nor loses.

The following is the level of revenue a company should have

VINOS DEL PACIFICO SA", therefore there are no gains or losses.

$$P.E = \frac{costos\ fijos}{1 - \frac{costos\ variables}{ventas}}$$

$$P.E = \frac{171429}{1 - \frac{543.468}{78960}}$$

P.E = 29.155

29,155 units must be sold to avoid incurring a loss. **4.11 ECONOMIC AND FINANCIAL EVALUATION**

a. Initial situation

Statement of the initial position of VINOS DEL PACIFICO S.A..

ACTIVITIES		DUTIES.	
Current assets		Non-current liabilities	50% NFC $
Banks	$ 59.024	Documents for payment	50.019
Total Current assets	**$ 59.024**	**Total non-current liabilities**	**$ 50.019**
Property, plant and equipment Machinery	$ 15.195	Legacy	$
and equipment Computer equipment	$ 3.360	Equity	50.019
Office furniture and equipment	$ 5.460	**Total capital**	**$ 50.019**
Vehicles	$ 15.000		
Total Property, plant and equipment	**$ 39.015**		
Deferred assets			
Expenses on formation	$ 2.000		
Total Deferred assets	**$ 2.000**		
TOTAL ASSETS	**$ 100.038**	**TOTAL LIABILITIES + EQUITY**	**$ 100.038**

b. Forecast income statement

PROJECTED INCOME STATEMENT					
Description	Year 1	Year 2	Year 3	Year 4	Year 5
Sales	$ 789.600	$ 802.080	$ 814.750	$ 827.620	$ 840.690
TOTAL INCOME	$ 789.600	$ 802.080	$ 814.750	$ 827.620	$ 840.690
(-) PRODUCTION COSTS					
Raw materials	$ 33.000	$ 33.363	$ 33.730	$ 34.101	$ 34.476
Direct materials	$ 394.890	$ 399.234	$ 403.625	$ 408.065	$ 412.554
Direct labor	$ 108.378	$ 110.778	$ 113.178	$ 115.578	$ 117.978
supplies	$ 7.200	$ 7.279	$ 7.539	$ 7.439	$ 7.520
(-)OPERATING EXPENSES					

Basic services and supplies	$ 2.640	$ 2.669	$ 2.698	$ 2.728	$ 2.758
Indirect labor	$ 25.200	$ 25.400	$ 25.600	$ 25.800	$ 26.000
Administrative expenses	$ 60.176	$ 60.876	$ 61.576	$ 62.276	$ 62.976
Other expenses	$ 76.800	$ 77.645	$ 78.499	$ 79.362	$ 80.235
Depreciation and amortization of assets	$ 2.317	$ 2.317	$ 2.317	$ 2.317	$ 2.317
Amortization of deferred assets	$ 400	$ 400	$ 400	$ 400	$ 400
Interest on loans	$ 3.896	$ 3.230	$ 2.511	$ 1.736	$ 900
TOTAL COSTS	$ 714.897	$ 723.191	$ 731.673	$ 739.802	$ 748.114
EARNINGS BEFORE EMPLOYEE BENEFITS	$ 74.703	$ 78.889	$ 83.077	$ 87.818	$ 92.576
(-) 15% Participation in laborers	11,21	11,83	12,46	13,18	13,89
PROFIT BEFORE INCOME TAX	$ 74.714	$ 78.877	$ 83.089	$ 87.805	$ 92.562
(-) Income tax 22%.	$ 16.437	$ 17.353	$ 18.279	$ 19.317	$ 20.364
NET PROFIT	$ 58.277	$ 61.524	$ 64.810	$ 68.488	$ 72.198

c. Projected cash flow

Projected cash flow					
Description	Period 0	Year 1	Year 2	Year 3	Year 4	Year 5
Operational flow						
Revenue in units		$ 78.960	$ 80.208	$ 81.475	$ 82.762	$ 84.069
Sales		$ 789.600	$ 802.080	$ 814.750	$ 827.620	$ 840.690
(-) expenditures						
Production costs		$ 543.468	$ 550.654	$ 558.072	$ 565.183	$ 572.528
Operating costs		$ 171.429	$ 172.537	$ 173.601	$ 174.619	$ 175.586
Net operating cash flow		$ 74.703	$ 78.889	$ 83.077	$ 87.818	$ 92.576
(-) depreciation and amortization expense		$ 2.317	$ 2.317	$ 2.317	$ 2.317	$ 2.317
(-) depreciation and amortization expense		$ 400	$ 400	$ 400	$ 400	$ 400
		$ 71.986	$ 76.172	$ 80.360	$ 85.101	$ 89.859

(-) 15% employee participation	$ 11	$ 12	$ 12	$ 13	$ 14
(-) 20% income tax	$ 16.437	$ 17.353	$ 18.279	$ 19.317	$ 20.364
(+) depreciation and amortization expense	$ 2.317	$ 2.317	$ 2.317	$ 2.317	$ 2.317
(+) amortization expense ad	$ 400	$ 400	$ 400	$ 400	$ 400
Net income	$ 58.255	$ 61.524	$ 64.786	$ 68.488	$ 72.198
Flow of finance					
Cash receipts					
(-) cash outflows Loans received					
Loan repayments (cf.)	$ 8.562	$ 9.229	$ 9.948	$ 10.723	11,557,96
Interest payment 7.79	$ 3.896	$ 3.230	$ 2.511	$ 1.736	$ 900
Net cash flow from Financing	$ 100.038	$ 12.458	$ 12.458	$ 12.458	$ 12.458	$ 12.458
Net cash flow	$ 100.038	$ 45.796	$ 49.066	$ 52.327	$ 56.030	$ 59.740
Accumulated cash flow	$ 100.038	$ 145.834	$ 194.900	$ 247.228	$ 303.257	$ 362.997

4.12 FINANCIAL ASSESSMENT

4.12.1 Net present value

Net present value is an investment criterion that consists of updating the receipts and disbursements of a project to know how much will be gained and lost.

The criterion states:

V   AN > 0 = investment is feasible

V   AN = 0 = indifferent investment

V   AN < 0 = Uncomfortable investment

A discount rate of 12% was used for this purpose.

PERIOD		CLEAN FLOW
	0	($ 100.038)
	1	$ 45.796
		$ 49.066
		$ 52.327
		$ 56.030
	5	$ 59.740
Total		

Table 55 Net present value
Source: Mana Fernanda Ladines and Diana Pineda, 2018

VAN	$86.717,88
IRR	41%

4.12.2 Internal rate of return

Assessment	
Net present value	$ 86.717,88
Internal rate of return	41%
Discount rate	12%

Table 56 Internal rate of return
Source: Mana Fernanda Ladines and Diana Pineda, 2018

CONCLUSIONS AND RECOMMENDATIONS

Conclusions

- Wine is a beverage made by fermenting fruit juice, in this case orange juice, which has beneficial properties.

- The creation of Vinos del Pacifico is profitable because according to the analysis of net present value and internal rate of return, the project is very profitable, as profits are generated already in the first year.

- The realization of this project justifies a profitable investment, as it will allow investors to obtain attractive profits, and the establishment of the company creates sources of employment and develops activities that contribute to the well-being of society.

- The marketing plan indicates that it is necessary to position the company in the market by emphasizing the quality, presentation and brand of the product at an attractive price and according to the economic situation of the product and meeting their needs, being class c (middle class) is the market to be reached.

- The technical study of this project allows investors to analyze the fundamental aspects of Caluma wine production, including the conditions of size and location of the enterprise to be created.

- The financial study presents project scenarios over the life of the project, reflecting 5-year projections of the most important indicators for the investor in terms of revenues, costs, expenses, deferred investment in fixed assets and financing.

- The ability of the business to generate future cash flows can be assessed, making it a viable investment project.

Recommendations

- Seek new markets in the national environment as the installed capacity in the plant of this project allows for large scale production, in the same way industrialize other fruits and thereby increase national production in the country.

- Maintain adequate quality control of raw materials and processes, ensuring they meet the requirements set by the client, in addition, the Caluma Wine production process must be under the responsibility of competent professionals to meet the objectives set by the organization.

- Train staff to achieve effective results in all processes, as they will

  highly qualified and motivated personnel, and therefore it is very important to

  It is very important to train each and every member of the Vinos del team Pacifico S.A. in any of the neighborhoods in which they are located.

- It is very important for Vinos del Pacifico S.A. to have good customer service, to have full feedback and loyalty with customers so that they are satisfied and loyal to our company.

- Producing on a large scale to reduce the cost of producing Caluma wine.

- Company expansion and innovation allows for the creation of new products that give access to revenue generation.

BIBLIOGRAPHIC REFERENCES

Abad, M. P. (n.d.). *Acenologia* . Retrieved from.
http://www.acenologia.com/cienciaytecnologia/cultura_patrimonio_vino_cienc0214.htm

Anzi, F. (August 12, 2016). *Zona Economica* . Retrieved from
https://www.zonaeconomica.com/estudio-financiero.

Barber, W. (March 10, 2013). *Viti viticulture* . Retrieved from.
http://www.vitivinicultura.net/clasificacion-de-los-vinos.html

Barber, W. (March 10, 2013). *Viti viticulture* . Retrieved from.
http://www.vitivinicultura.net/clasificacion-de-los-vinos.html

Barber, W. (March 10, 2013). Barber's *Nurseries* . Retrieved from.
http://www.vitivinicultura.net/clasificacion-de-los-vinos.html

Bembibre, K. (August 15, 2010). *ABC definition*. Retrieved from.
https://www.definicionabc.com/?s=Fermentaci%C3%B3n#resultados

Bembibre, K. (October 03, 2010). *Definition of ABC* . Retrieved from
https://www.definicionabc.com/general/naranja.php.

DefinicionMX. (May 8, 2017). *Derecho* . Retrieved from https://definicion.mx/derecho.

Encalada, P. (July 14, 2012). Wine is an alternative to frutfcola. *El Comercio newspaper,* pp. 1.

Leibl, P. Y. (July 24, 2003). *Protocol org*. retrieved from
https://www.protocolo.org/social/la-mesa/tipos-de-vino-clasificaciones.html

Gregorio, D. G. (2010). Concepts and methodology of historical research. *Revista Cubana de Salud Publica* , 36.

Guerrero, E. E. (1992). La definicion del negocio "Concepto tradicional y nuevo". *Innovar Journal Journal of Administrative and Social Sciences*.

Herrera, A. S. (March 14, 2012). *Colegio Oficial de Farmaceuticos de Cordoba COFCO.ORG*. Retrieved from http://www.cofco.org/ficheros/Naranja2.pdf.

INEC. (n.d.). *Ecuador in figures*. Retrieved from
http://www.ecuadorencifras.gob.ec//documentos/web-inec/Estadisticas_Sociales/Encuesta_Nac_Ingresos_Gastos_Hogares_Urb_Rur_ENIGHU/ENIG HU-2011-2012/EnighurPresentacionRP.pdf

KAREN AGUIRRE and JENNIFFER ALLAUCA . (April 2016). "BUSINESS PLAN FOR THE ESTABLISHMENT OF A NUTRIPAN BAKERY IN LA PUNTILLA - SAMBORONDON IN THE PROVINCE OF GUAYAS". Guayaquil.

LAPACHO. (2017). la tercera p plaza o distribución. *color abc*, 2.
http://www.abc.com.py/articulos/la-tercera-p-la-plaza-o-distribucion-936762.html

MARKETER02. (2014). i Do you know the difference between ATL-, BTL- and TTL-media? *SLOGAN MARKETING*, 2. Retrieved from
https://sloganmarketing.wordpress.com/2014/02/05/sabes- cual-es-la-diferencia-entre-medios-atl-btl-y-ttl/

Maidata, A. G. (2002). Wines, polyphenols and health protection. *Revista Cubana Aliment Nutr* , 141.

Melero, K. L. (June 2009). Retrieved from
http://rodin.uca.es/xmlui/bitstream/handle/10498/15775/Tes_2010_05.pdf

Orozco, H. d. (n.d.). *FINANCIAL EVALUATION OF PROJECTS.* ECOE Edition.

Patricio, Z. M. (2011). Retrieved from http://repositorio.utc.edu.ec/bitstream/27000/709/1/T-UTC- 0557.pdf

PHILIP Kotler and GARY Armstrong (2012). MARKETING . Mexico: PEARSON EDUCACION.

Piazza, S. B. (2017). *Antecedentes de los mercados del vino y de la uva vinifera.* chile: Oficina de Estudios y Polfticas Agrarias -Odepa. Retrieved from http://www.odepa.gob.cl/wp-content/uploads/2017/07/mercadoVino2017.pdf

Porter, M. E. (2008). Five competitive forces.

Ramnres, K. (February 14, 2011). *REDHECS.* Retrieved from.
http://publicaciones.urbe.edu/index.php/REDHECS/article/viewArticle/648/2302

Remash, H. E. (2015). Retrieved from http://repositorio.uteq.edu.ec/bitstream/43000/296/1/T-UTEQ- 0033.pdf

Rodnges, M. E. (2016). Retrieved from
http://repositorio.ucsg.edu.ec/bitstream/3317/5502/1/T- UCSG-PRE-TEC-CIA-8.pdf.

Salazar, T. (June 14, 2016). *The Connoisseur* . Retrieved from http://revistaelconocedor.com/la-relacion-del-vino-y-la-salud/

Salinas, P. H. (2010). *Research methodology.*

C - METHODS DIRECTORATE, A. E. (2014). *A SHEET OF COMMON FIGURES.* Calumet: SENPLADES.
Retrieved from http://app.sni.gob.ec/sni-.
link/sni/Portal%20SNI%202014/FICHAS%20F/0206_CALUMA_BOLIVAR.pdf

Smolek, A. (May 19, 2017). *Concha y Toro* . Retrieved from
https://www.conchaytoro.com/wine- blog/vinos-dulces-espumosos/.

Valentine (n.d.). *vix.* Retrieved from https://www.vix.com/es/imj/6128/beneficios-de-la-naranja

VELASQUEZ, K. (2015). i WHAT IS POSITIONING IN THE MARKET? *MARKETING ECOMMERCE MX*, 1. Retrieved from https://marketing4ecommerce.mx/que-es-el-posicionamiento-de- mercado/

Zurita, V. P. (2011).

APPENDICES.

Annex 1 Model of the survey to be used

Research

Gender: male female

Age:

a) 18-28

b) 29- 38

c) 39-48

d) 49-60

1. **What kind of beverage do you use?**

a) Whiskey

b) Beer

c) Wine

d) Vodka

2. **What kind of wine do you drink?**

a) Peach

b) Grapes

c) Orange

d) Apple

3. **How often do you consume wine?**

Daily

once a week

Every 15 days

once a month

4. What wine do you consume most often?

White

Pink

Red

Sparkling wines

5. Where do you buy your wine?

Larder (Shop, Minimarket) _____ Online Shop_____

LicorenaA gas   station Supermarket

6. For what occasions do you use this product?

Special occasions Meetings (home) Birthdays

Meals (lunch - dinner) Other

7. Please indicate the factor that is most important to you when choosing a good wine.

Price Taste/QualityDesign/presentation

Quality Brand Cercarna item/sales Country of origin

8. What country did you use wine from?

a) Argentina b) Chile

(c) Ecuador

(d) France

9. How much have you ever paid for wine?

a) $5-$10

b) $10- 15

c) $15-$20

d) $20-$30

10. What is your monthly income?

a) Base salary

b) 400 - 600

c) 600 - 800

d) 800 or more

11. Do you know about the health benefits of wine?

a) Bb   ) No

12. What kind of presentation would you like to see in a wine?

   a) Glass container.

   b) Tetra Park

   c) Biodegradable packaging

   d) Plastic container

13. Are you ready to consume orange wine produced in Ecuador?

   a) Bb   ) No

14. How much would you be willing to pay for 750ml of orange wine?

   a) $ 5 - $10d   ) 20 - 30

b) $10 - $15

c) $15 - 20

Annex 2 Vendor evaluation

SUPPLIER EVALUATION VINOS DEL PACIFICO S.A.

DATES:	CONTINUED				
EVALUATION NUMBER					
SUPPLIER INFORMATION					
VENDOR NAME OR COMPANY NAME	PAYMENT TERMS:				
COMPANY ADDRESS:	DISCOUNTS:				
CITY:	EST PHONE:				
ZIP CODE:					
MATERIAL OR SERVICE OFFERED:BY THE _____ SELLER:					
COMPLIES WITH THE REQUIREMENTS	1				5
IS A REPUTABLE COMPANY MEETS THE REQUIRED SPECIFICATIONS MANAGES AN AMPLE SUPPLY HAS A DEFINED DELIVERY TIME THE COMPANY CAN PROVIDE THE NECESSARY MATERIALS OR SERVICES THE COMPANY TRANSPORTS THE PRODUCTS TO OUR FACILITIES THE COMPANY GUARANTEES THAT THE MATERIALS WILL BE DELIVERED IN GOOD CONDITION. THE COMPANY COMPLIES WITH THE PRICES SET BY THE CUSTOMER. PRODUCT QUALITY COMPARED TO SPECIFICATIONS LEVEL OF RESEARCH AND DEVELOPMENT SUPPORT SALES STAFF EXPERIENCE THE COMPANY GIVES IMMEDIATE FEEDBACK ON QUOTES QUALITY OF SERVICE					
TOTAL					

Appendix 3 Product data sheet

VINOS DEL PACIFICO SA PRODUCT INFORMATION SHEET	
Product name: Responsible for inspection Date of inspection	
PRODUCT EVALUATION CRITERIA	
Organoleptic quality Color Flavor Flavor Sequence	
Physicochemical analysis Alcohol Sugar Volatile substances Acids	
PRESENTATION AND STORAGE CONDITIONS	
750 ml container glass bottle temperature 9 to 15°C	

Appendix 4 Risk Matrix Pacific Wines

	RISK MATRIX VINOS DEL PACIFICO SA				
Process/area identification	Detected risk	Frequency	Gravity (impact)	Value at risk	Level Risk
Reception operators				0	Minor
Pulp production operators				0	Minor
Fermentation Manager				0	Minor
Flotation operators				0	Minor
Packaging and sealing operators				0	Minor
Bodeguero				0	Minor
Prepared by	Approved				

Appendix 5 Amortization per month

Quota	credit balance	Capital	Interests	Value quota	Interest rate

1	$50,019.00	$833 .65	$ 312.62	$1,146.27	7.79%
	$49, 18535	$833 .65	$ 307.41	$ 1,141.06	7.79%
	$48, 351.70	$833 .65	$ 30220	$ 1,135.85	7.79%
	$47, 518.05	$833 .65	$ 296.99	$ 1,130.64	7.79%
5	$46, 684.40	$833 .65	$ 291.78	$ 1,125.43	7.79%
	$45 ,850.75	$833 .65	$ 286.57	$ 1,120.22	7.79%
	$45 ,017.10	$833 .65	$ 281.36	$ 1,115.01	7.79%
S	$44, 183.45	$833 .65	$ 276.15	$ 1,109.80	7.79%
	$43, 349.80	$833 .65	$ 270.94	$ 1,104.59	7.79%
10	$42, 516.15	$833 .65	$ 265.73	$ 1,099.38	7.79%
	$41 ,682.50	$833 .65	$ 260.52	$ 1,094.17	7.79%
	$40,848.85	$833 .65	$ 255.31	$ 1,088.96	7.79%
	$40,01520	$833 .65	$ 250.10	$ 1,083.75	7.79%
	$39 ,18135	$833 .65	$ 244.88	$ 1,078.53	7.79%
	$38 ,347.90	$833 .65	$ 239.67	$ 1,073.32	7.79%
	$37 ,51425	$833 .65	$ 234.46	$ 1,068.11	7.79%
	$36, 680.60	$833 .65	$ 229.25	$ 1,062.90	7.79%
IS	$35 ,846.95	$833 .65	$ 224.04	$ 1,057.69	7.79%
	$35 ,01330	$833 .65	$ 218.83	$ 1,052.48	7.79%
	$ 34,179.65	$833 .65	$ 213.62	$ 1,047.27	7.79%
21	$33 ,346.00	$833 .65	$ 208.41	$ 1,042.06	7.79%
	$32, 51235	$833 .65	$ 203.20	$ 1,036.85	7.79%
23	$31, 678.70	$833 .65	$ 197.99	$ 1,031.64	7.79%
	$30 ,845.05	$833 .65	$ 192.78	$ 1,026.43	7.79%
25	$30,011.40	$833 .65	$ 187.57	$ 1,021.22	7.79%
26	$ 29,177.75	$833 .65	$ 182.36	$ 1,016.01	7.79%
	$28 ,344.10	$833 .65	$ 177.15	$ 1,010.80	7.79%
	$27 ,510.45	$833 .65	$ 171.94	$ 1,005.59	7.79%
29	$26, 676.80	$833 .65	$ 166.73	$ 1,000.38	7.79%
30	$25,843.15	$833 .65	$ 161.52	$ 995.17	7.79%
31	$25,009.50	$833 .65	$ 156.31	$ 989.96	7.79%
	$ 24,175.85	$833 .65	$ 151.10	$ 984.75	7.79%
	$23, 34220	$ 833.65	$ 145.89	$ 979.54	7.79%

	$ 22,50855	$ 833.65	$ 140.68	$ 974.33	7.79%
35	$ 21,674.90	$ 833.65	$ 135.47	$ 969.12	7.79%
	$ 20,84125	$ 833.65	$ 130.26	$ 963.91	7.79%
	$ 20,007.60	$ 833.65	$ 125.05	$ 958.70	7.79%
	$ 19,173.95	$ 833.65	$ 119.84	$ 953.49	7.79%
	$ 18,34030	$ 833.65	$ 114.63	$ 948.28	7.79%
40	$ 17,506.65	$ 833.65	$ 109.42	$ 943.07	7.79%
	$ 16,673.00	$ 833.65	$ 104.21	$ 937.86	7.79%
42	$ 15,83935	$ 833.65	$ 99.00	$ 932.65	7.79%
43	$ 15,005.70	$ 833.65	$ 93.79	$ 927.44	7.79%
	$ 14,172.05	$ 833.65	$ 88.58	$ 922.23	7.79%

45	$ 13,338.40	$ 833.65	$ 83.37	8 917.02	7.79%
46	$ 12,504.75	$ 833.65	$ 78.15	8 911.80	7.79%
	$ 11,671.10	$ 833.65	$ 72.94	$ 906.59	7.79%
48	$ 10,837.45	$ 833.65	$ 67.73	$ 901.38	7.79%
49	$ 10,003.80	$ 833.65	$ 62.52	8 896.17	7.79%
50	$ 9,170.15	$ 833.65	$ 57.31	8 890.96	7.79%
51	$ 8336.50	$ 833.65	$ 52.10	8 885.75	7.79 %|
52	$ 7,502.85	8 833.65	$ 46.89	$ 880.54	7.79%
	$ 6,669.20	$ 833.65	$ 41.68	8 875.33	7.79%
	$ 5,835.55	$ 833.65	$ 36.47	$ 870.12	7.79%
55	$ 5,001.90	$ 833.65	$ 31.26	$ 864.91	7.79%
56	$ 4,168.25	8 833.65	$ 26.05	$ 859.70	7.79%
	$ 3334.60	8 833.65	$ 20.84	8 854.49	7.79%
58	$ 2,500.95	8 833.65	$ 15.63	$ 849.28	7.79%
59	$ 1,667.30	8 833.65	$ 10.42	$ 844.07	7.79%
	$ 833.65	8 833.65	$ ___ Print 521	$ 838.86	7.79%
		8 50,019.00	8 9,534.88	$ 59,553.88	

9 786206 988441